Gemini

22 May – 21 June

First published in Great Britain 2009
by Harlequin Mills & Boon Limited,
Eton House, 18-24 Paradise Road, Richmond, Surrey TW9 1SR

Copyright © Dadhichi Toth 2008 & 2009

ISBN: 978 0 263 87066 4

Typeset at Midland Typesetters Australia

Harlequin Mills & Boon policy is to use papers that are natural, renewable and recyclable products and made from wood grown in sustainable forests. The logging and manufacturing processes conform to the legal environmental regulations of the country of origin.

Printed and bound in Spain
by Litografia Rosés S.A., Barcelona

About
Dadhichi

Dadhichi is one of Australia's foremost astrologers. He has the ability to draw from complex astrological theory to provide clear, easily understandable advice and insights for people who want to know what their future might hold.

In the 26 years that Dadhichi has been practising astrology, face reading and other esoteric studies, he has conducted over 9,500 consultations. His clients include celebrities, political and diplomatic figures, and media and corporate identities from all over the world.

Dadhichi's unique blend of astrology and face reading helps people fulfil their true potential. His extensive experience practising western astrology is complemented by his research into the theory and practice of eastern systems of astrology.

Dadhichi features in numerous newspapers and magazines and he also appears regularly on many of Australia's leading television and radio networks, where many of his political and worldwide forecasts have proved uncannily accurate.

His website www.astrology.com.au is now one of the top ten online Australian lifestyle sites and, in conjunction with www.facereader.com, www.soulconnector.com and www.psychjuice.com, they attract over half a million visitors monthly. The websites offer a wide variety of features, helpful information and personal services.

Dedicated to The Light of Intuition

Sri V. Krishnaswamy—mentor and friend

With thanks to Julie, Joram, Isaac and Janelle

Welcome from
Dadhichi

Dear Friend,

Welcome! It's great to have you here, reading your horoscope, trying to learn more about yourself and what's in store for you in 2010.

I visited Mexico a while ago and stumbled upon the Mayan prophecies for 2012, which, they say, is the year when the longstanding calendar we use in the western world supposedly stops! If taken literally, some people could indeed believe that 'the end of the world is near'. However, I see it differently.

Yes, it might seem as though the world is getting harder and harder to deal with, especially when fear enters our lives. But, I believe that 'the end' indicated by these Mayan prophecies has more to do with the end that will create new beginnings for our societies, more to do with making changes to our material view of life and some necessary adjustments for the human race to progress and prosper in future. So let's get one thing straight: you and I will both be around after 2012, reading our 2013 horoscopes!

My prediction and advice centres around keeping a cool mind and not reacting to the fear that could overtake us. Of course, this isn't easy, especially when media messages might increase our anxiety about such things as the impacts of global warming or the scarcity of fossil fuels.

I want you to understand that it is certainly important to be aware and play your part in making the world a better place; however, the best and surest way to support global goals is to help yourself first. Let me explain. If everyone focused just a little more on improving *themselves* rather than just pointing their finger to criticise others, it would result in a dramatic change and improvement; not just globally, but societally. And, of course, you mustn't forget what a positive impact this would have on your personal relationships as well.

Astrology focuses on self-awareness; your own insights into your personality, thinking processes and relationships. This is why this small book you have in your hand doesn't only concentrate on what is going to happen, but more importantly how you can *make* things happen positively through being your best.

I have always said that there are two types of people: puppets and actors. The first simply react to each outside stimulus and are therefore slaves of their environment, and even of their own minds and emotions. They are puppets in the hands of karma. The other group I call actors. Although they can't control what happens to them all the time, either, they are better able to adapt and gain something purposeful in their lives. They are in no way victims of circumstance.

I hope you will use what is said in the following pages to become the master of your destiny, and not rely on the predictions that are given as mere fate but as valuable guidelines to use intelligently when life presents you with its certain challenges.

Neither the outside world, nor the ups and downs that occur in your life, should affect your innermost spirituality and self-confidence. Take control: look beyond your current challenges and use them as the building blocks of experience to create success and fulfilment in the coming year.

I believe you have the power to become great and shine your light for all to see. I hope your 2010 horoscope book will be a helpful guide and inspiration for you.

Warm regards, and may the stars shine brightly for you in 2010!

Your Astrologer,

Dadhichi Toth

Contents

The Gemini
Identity

The first step in the acquisition of wisdom is silence, the second listening, the third memory, the fourth practice, the fifth teaching others.

—Solomon Gabriol

Gemini: A Snapshot

Key Characteristics

Versatile, intellectual, communicative, social, scattered, many interests, love of variety and change

Compatible Star Signs

Aries, Leo, Libra, Sagittarius, Aquarius

Key Life Phrase

I think

Life Goals

To be respected for your intelligence; to be creatively original

Platinum Assets

Lightning-quick reflexes, multi-tasker, inspirational and fun

Zodiac Totem

The Twins

Zodiac Symbol

♊

Zodiac Facts

Third sign of the zodiac; mutable, masculine and positive, barren

Element

Air

Famous Geminis

Jamie Oliver, Kylie Minogue, Lenny Kravitz, John F. Kennedy, Steve Waugh, Brooke Shields, Meryl Streep, Anna Kournikova, Tim Allen, Venus Williams, Walt Whitman, Sir Paul McCartney, Drew Carey, Johnny Depp, Angelina Jolie, Annette Bening, Colin Farrell, Barbara Bush, Donald Trump, Ice Cube, Bob Dylan, Errol Flynn, Priscilla Presley

Gemini: Your profile

If you happen to be sitting at a party and you see a whirlwind coming, it's quite likely a Gemini. Full of gusto, versatility and energy, the Gemini individual is larger than life and more often than not engaged in doing seven or eight things at once.

Keeping up with you is not an easy thing for most people. You have a quick wit, exceedingly fast speech, and quirky, original expressions that others sometimes don't understand. Many brilliantly successful people are born under your star sign and this reflects their amazing creativity and innovative approach to life.

Part of your trademark personality is your extraordinary ability to communicate ideas and to develop new lines of thinking. Your mind is always on the go, drawing on all sorts of life experiences and interesting information. You love facts, figures and the whys and wherefores of life. Often, however, you tend to overload your mind and this is something you need to watch. You can weigh yourself down with so much information that at times you run yourself ragged. Try to develop your powers of discrimination so that you can filter out what's necessary and what's not.

Because of your immense curiosity, you will never stop learning. You will constantly be interested in developing your base of knowledge and deepening your awareness of the world and people generally. Your intellect is sharp like a knife and cuts through some of the most difficult problems; but this is also a problem for you, in that you get bored easily and are constantly on the lookout for more exciting and stimulating experiences. If others don't provide this to you, you are quick to move on to bigger and better things.

You have a restless nature and always seem to be on the go. It doesn't feel quite right when you don't have something or other to do. Doing nothing is the worst thing for a Gemini. You must agree, however, that this can tire you out and possibly even affect your health from time to time. Therefore, try to find suitable outlets to channel your highly strung nature. Any sort of physical sport or outdoor activity will help minimise these problems and get you back on track.

You know all too well that the schizophrenic jokes about Gemini are true, to some extent. There are two sides to your nature and this is due to the fact that Gemini is a dual, or what is known as a mutable, sign. You constantly oscillate between the highs and the lows, the light and the dark, and the ups and the downs of your personality through life's twists and turns.

You prefer the variety and spice of life rather than cold comfort and the 'same old same old'. You have an absorptive mind and grasp ideas very quickly. Words are of interest to you, so you'd make a great writer or at least an avid reader.

Travel is strongly linked to your star sign so your restless spirit will find great satisfaction in journeying and exploring the world. Throughout your life you will explore many different places and probably move around quite a bit to satisfy your innate curiosity.

Three classes of Gemini

If you were born between the 22nd of May and the 1st of June, you are primarily an intellectual type of individual, whose main forte is communication. You enjoy reading and learning about anything and everything. You have quick mental reflexes and versatility in communication.

Being born between the 2nd and the 12th of June, you will be a more sensual and emotional type of Gemini. Unlike other Geminis, your feelings may overtake your mental judgement and so these often need to be kept in check. Venus, the planet of love, has a strong rulership over your destiny.

If you happen to be born between the 13th and the 21st of June, you're a Gemini who has a rather wild and whacky side to your personality. You have a great sense of humour and people love to be in your company. Life will generally never be at all boring for you.

Gemini role model: Kylie Minogue

Kylie Minogue, the now internationally acclaimed pop star, began her journey as a humble actress on an Australian soapie program. Her communication, creative enterprise and brilliant onstage performances reflect perfectly the Gemini personality. Like her, most Geminis possess an incredible load of talent in many different areas.

Gemini: The light side

My experiences with Geminis have always led me to believe that their minds are light years ahead of most of us. Sometimes you'll have to pretend that you understand where they're coming from because their level of understanding is so broad and diverse. Not only that, you'll need lightning-fast reflexes to keep up with the pace of their conversations.

Yes, it's true. You have an original and brilliant mind but hopefully you're learning to direct that in constructive ways.

You have a natural affinity with people and are the consummate networker. You love getting out and about among people, and communication is by far your greatest asset. Coupled with your enthusiasm, you have no problem making friends and achieving success in life.

Being the twin sign of the zodiac means you're able to argue both sides of a discussion, but this also makes it difficult for you to be decisive at times.

You are adaptable, flexible and feel comfortable pretty much anywhere.

Gemini: The shadow side

Being a dual sign means having two distinctly different aspects to your character, which can make life hard for you occasionally. You could be regarded as the proverbial Dr Jekyll and Mr Hyde, couldn't you?

There are so many facets to your nature that even you find it hard to keep up with yourself! You're ruled by the planet Mercury, which is where the term 'mercurial' comes from; slipping and sliding in and out of life's many colourful situations seems to be the typical Gemini life pattern. But this may also reflect to some extent the old saying that 'the rolling stone gathers no moss'.

Certainly, your love of variety and change leads you to an exciting life, but the danger is that you could become 'a jack-of-all-trades, and a master of none'. Spending a little time planning your days, weeks and months will be the perfect recipe for success for the typical Gemini.

You have a need to do as much as you can, but this impulsive streak may become your undoing. Try to bite off smaller chunks of life so that you don't have to chew so fast to digest it.

Gemini woman

Not all women born under Gemini are as scattered as most astrological books would lead you to believe. Sure, if you're a female Gemini reading this, you'd have to agree that in the earlier part of your life you were probably categorised under the heading 'airhead'. But this is only because of your passionate love of knowledge, thirst for life's experiences and the great joy you receive from sharing your ideas. It could probably be said in your defence that you think others are simply mounds of wet leather—or probably as boring as that. You don't mind being labelled in this way because you realise that life is about living, exploring and enjoying as much of it as you can.

You're a natural-born entertainer and this is because when you're in the company of others you have a natural flair for words and also a quick knack of understanding those around you. You love creating a fun environment and can make others feel at ease simply by your presence. You also have the ability to stimulate and open up others to the science of human possibilities. You are the catalyst for all sorts of communicative interaction.

Gemini women have all sorts of fascinating styles, but one thing is for certain: their personalities will always amaze those with whom they come in contact.

You are a creative, if not ingenious character, as shown by many other famous personalities born under your star sign. Versatile personalities such as Angelina Jolie, Anne Hash, Annette Bening and the wild and whacky Joan Rivers all share your Gemini birth sign and reveal the brilliance of Mercury.

The Gemini woman is usually very eye-catching. You're attractive, and you know it. But this may not always be the classical concept of beauty, rather more because of the electricity you exude. People find this irresistible and you have no problem finding love, or at least attracting the attention of romantic partners. Your up-beat, dynamic and spontaneous energy draws people to you and they often look up to you as a result. You are able to generate immense amounts of positive energy among your peers.

Those of you born in the earlier part of Gemini also possess some of the elements of Taurus. You are born on the cusp, making you even more sensual and attractive due to the influence of Venus.

You are probably quite well read or have had many life experiences that make you fascinating to be with. You can captivate others with your interesting stories and anecdotes. Although you listen to others (sometimes), you're also quite provocative and unafraid of a challenge. You can pick a fake a mile away and have no problem telling it as it is.

This will find you often embroiled in heated discussions, but you have no problem with this and, in fact, relish the idea of debate.

The Gemini woman rarely ages as fast as other women. Your positive mental attitude, your genetic physical structure and other factors seem to preserve your youthfulness, even into older age. Many Gemini women feel flattered by being told that they look ten or more years younger than they are!

Let your imagination soar, because you have plenty of it, and this will fuel your desire for success in life. By harnessing your great mental powers, your ability to negotiate with people and your natural attractiveness and charm, you will no doubt be a successful and loved person throughout life.

Gemini man

As with females born under Gemini, men of the same star sign are just as mentally powerful and probably as restless physically, too.

It's hard to keep up with your timetable and, unless you have a dozen projects on the go at once, you probably feel as if you're lazy and not quite as productive as you should be.

Gemini men tend to be highly strung but clear in what they want to achieve, even if they don't always meet their deadlines due to the heavy schedule they set themselves. You are a go-getter and therefore are prepared for the stress and tension your lifestyle throws at you.

You could be considered a chameleon by nature because you adapt yourself so easily to any situation or person you need to deal with. You have an extraordinary love of independence so others must be prepared to give you quite a wide berth if they choose to become involved with you. Others will be quite unsuccessful if they try to burden you with their schedules or timetables because you are a free-thinking and totally unfettered personality.

The versatility and independence of Gemini is clearly seen in someone like Clint Eastwood. I was amazed to read the credits on one of his recent movies, Million Dollar Baby. Clint wrote the movie, starred in it, directed it and even composed the music! Now, that's Gemini versatility for you.

Although you may be attracted to what money can buy, you will always place your intellectual and spiritual pursuits at the top of your list of life's priorities. You take great pride in doing your work well; but here again you must be careful not to cut corners due to the heavy demands you make on yourself.

You love innovation and anything original. You seek out new experiences because, to you, this is the stuff of which life is made. You get a great thrill from discovering new things and this, to you, is real knowledge, not what is taken from books, because there the text is second-hand. Although, you do enjoy a good book based on facts as well!

Gemini men are accused of being emotionally distant and aloof and, in relationships, your partners may find you a little hard to understand. This is only because you have so much going on in that brain of yours. You're restless and when it comes to making commitments you find it hard to surrender your interests in favour of some other interest. You will need to compartmentalise your emotional responsibilities and your mental interests clearly. A little more work can always be done in this area.

The Gemini man is a traveller and I've met many who, if they don't in fact work in some travel-related industry, will be forever jet setting from one country to another to explore the cultures and traditions of those places. Apart from this, you're always on the go and so travel may simply be part and parcel of your day-to-day existence.

Gemini child

Your Gemini child is a ball of energy! Their curious and intellectual abilities are evident from day one. Amazing little people, these Gemini kids will keep you on your toes, especially intellectually. So you'd better be prepared to handle their incessant stream of questions.

Being a parent of a Gemini child, you'll need to be physically fit yourself, just to keep up with them. They seem to have an endless supply of energy due to their restless nature.

Gemini kids love to play jokes and have a wonderful sense of humour. If you're a communicative parent and interact well with them, you'll have many hours of fun sharing jokes and playing pranks on each other.

The one great thing about having a Gemini child is that they love to share their feelings and their thoughts with you. This will draw you closer to each other and ensures an open and transparent relationship as they grow older.

Keep your Gemini child busily engaged with plenty of tasks, puzzles and other games to help them direct their vibrant little minds into constructive and useful pastimes. Gemini children have an insatiable thirst for knowledge and should do well at school, as long as you give them plenty to occupy them. Your Gemini child burns energy quicker than they can create it, so make sure they eat well and get plenty of rest. It's not a good idea to let them dictate what time they go to bed. Set down a schedule they can stick to and you will see just how much happier and healthier they are.

As the child of Gemini grows older, you'll realise that they must have some boundaries set for them so that they don't overstep their mental and physical endurance levels. Counsel them wisely so that they learn to do one thing at a time, and to do it properly. Help them to select their friends carefully. Gemini children want to be all things to all people, but you know as well as I do that this is not always possible.

Romance, love and marriage

The basis of any successful relationship is open, honest communication. Fortunately for you, Gemini, this is one of your most natural and in-built personality traits. This means it's only natural for you to want to communicate your ideas and feelings to the ones you love.

Gemini is an air sign, which rules the mental aspects of human nature and, although you do communicate well, you may have the tendency at times to let your head overrule your heart. You tend to filter your feelings through your mind and need to get more in touch with some emotional instincts if you are to take your relationships to the next level.

Although you never have a problem connecting with people generally and making many friends and new acquaintances, the idea of commitment does tend to scare you a little. You have a desire to be free and independent and, as long as your partner can afford you the space to grow as an individual, then maybe, just maybe, the big 'C' word won't terrify you too much.

You have an incredibly versatile personality and love variety. Sticking to one relationship might be difficult for this reason as well. You love the experience of exploring the world, meeting people and trying different things. You see this as a way of expanding your mind and would love your partner to view life in the same way. Sometimes, however, in marriage and/or a committed relationship, you could find that it's not always easy to do this once the day-to-day grind sets in and your family responsibilities take over. It would take a very special type of person to give you the freedom to continue along this sort of lifestyle and you only hope that when the right person comes along they too have a similar desire to live a free and exciting life with you.

True love to you means being free enough to express yourself on all levels—intellectually, physically and emotionally. Because your mind is such a dominant part of your being, it's quite likely that creative visualisation and fantasising will play a prominent role in your love life. Sharing this aspect of your sensual and sexual fantasies with another requires a high degree of trust, wouldn't you agree?

Ideally your soulmate will understand and encourage your diverse interests and your sometimes rather unbelievable ambitions. For you, a married partner needs to connect with your ideals and aspirations and support you in attaining these extraordinary life goals.

There are times when your Gemini mind just can't help being cynical, and this is one aspect of your personality that needs to be checked when and if you embark on your love life. Your critical nature is never meant to hurt others, although at times a touch of sarcasm will be thrown in to make your point. Usually, however, you have the other person's best interests at heart and generally want to help them grow and become happy and fulfilled within themselves.

It's important to understand that not everyone is as intellectual as you are and relating to others on a feeling level as well as a mental or intellectual level is a superior way of helping them.

You do tend to impose your opinions on others and, in the extreme, people can perceive you as an opinionated and even a self-righteous type of character. You find this amusing; but remember, being in a committed relationship is a long-term effort and this aspect of your nature may not be tolerated by the one you consider your soulmate. Try listening a little more to get to know how others are reacting to what you have to say.

When all is said and done you are a loyal, passionate and exciting person to be with and the energy you bring to a relationship is formidable. Once you consider someone worthy of your love you sacrifice a great deal for them; but the question is usually one of endurance with a Gemini. As long as your partner can satisfy your desire for variety and novelty, you will be able to make the commitment and hang in there for the long haul.

Health, wellbeing and diet

If you are a typical Gemini you generally don't put on too much weight and in fact find it quite easy to burn off calories due to your high metabolic rate. Other star signs probably envy you for this reason. If you're a typical Gemini, you're probably a little leaner than the rest of your zodiac cousins, so this in itself is a great indicator of health and overall vitality.

Running on your nerves, you risk burnout and many Geminis I have come in contact with do at times suffer from mental exhaustion and other nerve or stress-related issues.

Take time for the simple things, including sleep and a generally slower pace in life. Restore some balance to your frazzled nerves and make each mealtime one that is not a race to the finish line.

Gemini, being an air sign, rules the lungs, bronchial tubes, shoulders, arms and hands, so you must pay careful attention to your breathing so that your oxygen intake is adequate and can supply sufficient blood to these organs. It's not a good idea for Gemini to smoke because you also have the natural constitutional weakness that can lead to bronchitis, asthma and other pulmonary problems.

On a dietary level, certain foods produce digestive complications and this can result in flatulence and other metabolic disturbances. Try not to mix protein and starchy foods together in large quantities. Study books to learn how diet can affect your body and look to your own experiences.

Don't overdo sport because moderate exercise is better for you. Light walking, tennis, swimming and yoga are ideal.

Lean, high-protein foods are also a wonderful way for you to increase your level of energy. Oats and other grains such as muesli are the perfect start to the day. Make sure you eat breakfast each morning.

Work

Because of your natural tendency to think and act, work is a perfect outlet for you to express your creative mind.

As long as your chosen profession offers you sufficient creative input, variety and physical mobility, you'll be happy. If you choose an entre-preneurial line of work or something related to sales and marketing, you'll have the opportunity to display your social skills and make money at the same time.

Gemini is a dextrous zodiac sign therefore working with your hands will also give you satisfaction.

Being highly independent, many Gemini-born individuals excel at managing their own business and can do quite well at it.

You are a person of tremendous initiative and inspire others. Although you are quite demanding and have high standards, you make a great boss. However, you must learn to delegate the simple tasks so you don't become overwhelmed.

Teaching, typing, writing, acting, journalism, travel-related industries and any other line of work that requires mental input would be a great choice for you as a lifelong profession.

Key to karma, spirituality and emotional balance

In your past lives Aquarius had a strong impact on your character and in this life Aquarius's intel-lectual development is noticeable through you. Air signs such as yours are predominately concerned with thought power. Therefore, your key words are 'I think'.

Your lucky days

Your luckiest days are Wednesdays, Fridays and Saturdays.

Your lucky numbers

Remember that the forecasts given later in the book will help you optimise your chances of winning. Your lucky numbers are:

5, 14, 23, 32, 41, 50

6, 15, 24, 33, 42, 51

8, 17, 26, 35, 44, 53

Your destiny years

Your most important years are 5, 14, 23, 32, 41, 50, 59, 77, 86

Star Sign
Compatibility

*Happiness grows at our own firesides, and is not to be
picked in strangers' gardens.*

—Douglas Jerrold

Romantic compatibility

How compatible are you with your current partner,
lover or friend? Did you know that astrology can
reveal a whole new level of understanding between
people simply by looking at their star sign and that
of their partner? In this chapter I'd like to share
some special insights that will help you better
appreciate your strengths and challenges using Sun
sign compatibility.

The Sun reflects your drive, willpower and
personality. The essential qualities of two star signs
blend like two pure colours, producing an entirely
new colour. Relationships, similarly, produce their
own emotional colours when two people interact.
The following is a general guide to your romantic
prospects with others and how, by knowing the
astrological 'colour' of each other, the art of love
can help you create a masterpiece.

When reading the following I ask you to remember
that no two star signs are ever *totally* incompatible.
With effort and compromise, even the most 'difficult' astrological matches can work. Don't close
your mind to the full range of life's possibilities!
Learning about each other and ourselves is the
most important facet of astrology.

Quick-reference guide: Horoscope compatibility between signs (percentage)

	Aries	Taurus	Gemini	Cancer	Leo	Virgo	Libra	Scorpio	Sagittarius	Capricorn	Aquarius	Pisces
Aries	60	65	65	65	90	45	70	80	90	50	55	65
Taurus	60	70	70	80	70	90	75	85	50	95	80	85
Gemini	70	70	75	60	80	75	90	60	75	50	90	50
Cancer	65	80	60	75	70	75	60	95	55	45	70	90
Leo	90	70	80	70	85	75	65	75	95	45	70	75
Virgo	45	90	75	75	75	70	80	85	70	95	50	70
Libra	70	75	90	60	65	80	80	85	80	85	95	50
Scorpio	80	85	60	95	75	85	85	90	80	65	60	95
Sagittarius	90	50	75	55	95	70	80	85	85	55	60	75
Capricorn	50	95	50	45	45	95	85	65	55	85	70	85
Aquarius	55	80	90	70	70	50	95	60	60	70	80	55
Pisces	65	85	50	90	75	70	50	95	75	85	55	80

Each star sign combination is followed by the elements of those star signs and the result of their combining. For instance, Aries is a fire sign and Aquarius is an air sign and this combination produces a lot of 'hot air'. Air feeds fire and fire warms air. In fact, fire requires air. However, not all air and fire combinations work. I have included information about the different birth periods within each star sign and this will throw even more light on your prospects for a fulfilling love life with any star sign you choose.

Good luck in your search for love, and may the stars shine upon you in 2010!

Compatibility quick-reference guide

Each of the twelve star signs has a greater or lesser affinity with one another. The quick-reference guide will show you who's hot and who's not so hot as far as your relationships are concerned.

GEMINI + ARIES
Air + Fire = Hot Air

The romantic combination of Gemini and Aries is generally considered quite reasonable, given your elemental representations of fire and air. These two elements work well together because the oxygen of Gemini fuels the fire of Aries.

You will easily inflame the passion of Aries with your stimulating and exciting manner; however, it's quite likely you will soon discover a cultural rift between you.

Aries is not quite as refined as you are, in your estimation. This is not casting any doubts on the Aries brother- or sisterhood, but you prefer a more refined and polished type of individual as a partner rather than someone as reactive and at times as abrasive as Aries.

Having said this, you'll make great mates and you will from time to time support each other with encouragement and social activity.

Aries is quick off the mark and, although you can be a little impatient with them, you like the way they can move as swiftly as you do. There are moments of intensity between the combination of your star signs; but then, you'd far prefer this excitement than someone who is boring. At other times you'll both feel perfectly synchronised with each other's thoughts and feelings.

Aries is one of the most physical star signs and therefore you'll have your work cut out for you trying to keep up with them. You don't have the physical stamina of Aries but your mind is probably a step ahead of them and so you'll be able to compete with them through your sheer willpower. In trying to keep up with them, don't push yourself beyond your limits.

You can feel fulfilled sexually with Aries because, like you, they are young at heart and playful with life. You excite each other and enjoy exploring different ways of stimulating your bodies and your minds.

You like the idea of originality in your sexual exploits because this keeps your passion alive. Aries will be more than happy to play along and, if you are able to bridge that cultural gap I mentioned earlier, it's likely your relationship will be a satisfying one.

Aries born between the 21st and the 30th of March will make great friends. You feel a natural affinity with them and won't be afraid to share your feelings. You both need to have a great network of friends and social contacts if you want this partnership to get even better.

Aries born between the 31st of March and the 10th of April are also good friends and you'll have a fantastic rapport with them. In your business or commercial association with them you'll work well to create joint success. You understand each other and can be mutually supportive when the going gets tough.

With an Aries born between the 11th and the 20th of April, you make an excellent couple. Their co-ruler Jupiter is your karmic marriage planet and therefore, if you're considering a long-term relationship, here are partners who will satisfy you deeply.

GEMINI + TAURUS
Air + Earth = Dust

The pace of being a Gemini is hugely at odds with the slow and steady, meandering lifestyle of Taurus. This is your first problem in dealing with a Taurus partner.

Life with a Gemini is always hectic and Taurus will find this frustrating. They are the plodders of the zodiac whereas you, Gemini, are the consummate multi-tasker.

You need to take into account that Taurus is a rather stubborn type of individual and intellectually and romantically their attitudes will seem to be a little 'stuck in the mud' as far as you're concerned. Nevertheless, there is something to be said for the persevering and loyal side of Taurus and this is something that may just pull together your fast, scattered and impulsive nature.

Doing one thing at a time at the pace of Taurus will irritate you, frustrate you no end, and this will be a problem unless you regard this relationship as some sort of spiritual test for overcoming the rather scatty elements of your personality. If you're on the path of self-improvement then the challenge may well be worth it.

Gemini and Taurus do have a tendency to attract each other, however. The reason for this is that your ruling planets of Mercury and Venus are friendly by nature and, once you bring your minds into harmony, there can be brilliant moments of happiness, humour and fun together.

On an intimate level you may be too much of a fast mover for steady Taurus, who is slow to warm to your passionate interludes. Yet again, patience will be your key word if you're really trying to make this relationship work. Your mentally stimulating conversation will be the perfect antidote to an unresponsive Taurean. And, if you do happen to be a responsive Gemini, taking up this challenge could be a lot of fun for you. But don't expect any quick fixes in the bedroom.

If your Taurus mate has their birthday between the 21st and the 29th of April, this is a reasonably good combination. However, due to your intellectual ways, they may feel as if you overpower them. They are pretty smart, too, so don't underestimate their brilliance.

By far the best match with a Gemini is a Taurus born between the 30th of April and the 10th of May. Their birth dates are strongly affected by Mercury, which also rules you. You mirror many of each other's qualities, especially that playful aspect of your Gemini character.

Those born between the 11th and the 21st of May will have a very steadying influence on you. In short bursts you'll have a great time with them but could start to feel a little smothered by their Taurean possessiveness after a while.

GEMINI + GEMINI
Air + Air = Wind

If Gemini is a twin and you become involved with another Gemini, it appears to me that there'll be four people involved in this relationship, right? This is a versatile combination with an immense amount of potential but, with so many dual personalities interacting with each other, the going can also get rather tough.

Communication is your forte so naturally you can expect an amazing amount of interaction verbally between the two of you. Your diverse interests will most definitely keep this relationship alive as you both strive to stimulate each other and learn more and more about yourselves through your partnership.

Gemini is duplicitous, which means there are parts of your nature that you like to keep hidden from each other. There could be quite a few coveted secrets, which may be something that rears its head down the track and causes you both heartache when you least expect it. For that reason, the best policy for a relationship between two Geminis is to lay your cards out on the table early in the piece so as to avoid these emotional problems later.

Gemini is an insomniac by nature. You probably wake up late at night, coming up with all sorts of wild and wonderful ideas. But don't be surprised to wake up and find your Gemini partner staring at you with exactly the same problem. You'll spend many a night talking through your problems and sharing these ideas, if not utilising these opportunities to get closer physically. This will work for both of you.

If there are problems in the Gemini–Gemini relationship, the one saving grace is that you have humour. Usually Gemini can see the brighter side of life, even if everything is going against them. You'll support each other and use this element of your personality to lift the other, and vice versa. You'll experience great understanding through the power of your words and therefore the long-term forecast for your relationship is not bad at all.

Geminis born between the 22nd of May and the 1st of June make great partners because you have similar mental and social interests. Your communication sometimes will be in conflict, as your egos will vie for the top position. Generally, however, you'll have a good time being in each other's company.

If you are with another Gemini born between the 2nd and the 12th of June, this relationship will be much more sensual and compatible emotionally and physically. You'll be sensitive to each other's physical needs and your sexual activity will be the highlight of the time you spend together.

Geminis born between the 13th and the 21st of June are old souls and this relationship will definitely be karmic. There's a spiritual connection between you and some of life's deeper issues will be worked out together. You find it easier to talk to them and this is an enjoyable partnership that will bring you both fulfilment.

GEMINI + CANCER
Air + Water = Rain

You were born under the element of air, whereas Cancer is born under the element of water. These elements just don't mix. If you feel you don't understand the sensitive and changeable moods of Cancer, it's probably due to this simple, elemental astrological fact.

Your initial hurdle with Cancer lies in the fact that you try to convey your feelings through a rational, verbal approach. You'll be confused when Cancer doesn't respond in the way you expect. This has to do with the fact that the emotional responses of Cancer are sometimes operating on a subtle and even psychic level. You need to listen to Cancer with your heart, not your ears.

Cancer is one of the most loving and nurturing of the star signs, so you'll never be in short supply of hugs and kisses and security in their company. Your restlessness will create uneasiness for Cancer because they are primarily concerned with safety and being assured of a stable lifestyle. This is not to say that they don't enjoy the challenge of spontaneity, like you do. But they do need a solid base from which to operate and your scattered approach leaves them doubting you can provide this.

Cancer is adaptable and more open than you at first believe and this is something you'll also enjoy about them. On the other hand, they are ruled by the changeable Moon, which means you should expect moodiness and hypersensitivity to be part and parcel of your relationship with them. Even if you try to talk them through these moods, it will be to no avail. Remember, they are not necessarily amenable to solving problems from a mind level. You're just going to have to adjust yourself to the Cancer program and start to feel a little more.

Between the sheets, you'll feel loved and nurtured and will enjoy the genuine warmth that Cancer brings to your sexual connection. Talk a little less and try to feel the heart level of Cancer when you physically engage with them, and this will increase the intensity of your love for each other.

A Cancer born between the 22nd of June and the 3rd of July is a powerful financial stimulator but doesn't excite you emotionally. Working together and sharing commercial ideas might be the first step to taking the relationship to another level if you can both hang in there long enough.

Cancerians born between the 4th and the 13th of July are intense and will challenge your thinking and way of looking at things. There's a certain amount of volatility with individuals born in this period and you may not quite understand the strength of their moods. This will be a significant hurdle for you.

Cancers born between the 14th and the 22nd of July are not quite as difficult to handle so this could be a relationship worth considering. On the whole you'll be able to steer Cancer onto a more intellectual path and they in turn will help you get in touch with the spiritual side of your being.

GEMINI + LEO
Air + Fire = Hot Air

Gemini has a need to exert influence through displaying mental versatility so in a way you have an affinity with Leo, who is the performer of the zodiac. Both of you take pride in your achievements and finding the right partner is no exception as a means displaying how well you can do.

Having the right partner is important to you, but it is equally important to Leo. They will feel privileged and extremely happy to connect with someone who's not only able to express themselves but likes to tell them how great they are. You can do that. But this may wear a little thin if you feel as if the Leo ego is a bottomless pit, requiring flattery day in, day out. Hey, Gemini needs a little accolade here and there as well, don't you?

You need to bridge the gap between the huge ego of Leo and your need for recognition as well. Leo is often so self-absorbed as to overlook these needs and this will frustrate you.

As a team in a social context you work well. Leo is a shining light and together you can entertain, amuse and attract many friends and well-wishers. You have the gift of the gab and they have very powerful auras, which make them the centre of attraction. Together you will act as a supernova, attracting, almost magnetically, amazing people and circumstances into your lives.

Gemini and Leo are considered friendly by virtue of the zodiacal placements. You are in fact a great supporter of Leo and they can gain on many levels through their association with you. Financial opportunities can't be excluded, either. Business should prosper for the two of you as your luck extends into many spheres of life.

Leo does appreciate what you bring to the relationship but you'll need to be a little more organised to satisfy them fully. They can be demanding and inflexible, wanting things done exactly the way they want. Luckily for you, you have an adjustable personality and so you'll be able to cope with that.

Sexually, you excite each other and therefore, on many levels, including one of intimate involvement, the Gemini–Leo relationship stands a good chance of succeeding.

Average results are likely with Leos born between the 24th of July and the 4th of August. You mustn't expect this relationship to take off too quickly because it does have some initial obstacles. You need to listen carefully to each other.

There'll be combative episodes between you and Leos born between the 15th and 23rd of August. You both tend to be hell-bent on pushing your own ideas on each other and so this type of competition may not be altogether that healthy. These are the sorts of power games that will end up draining you both mentally and emotionally.

If you're looking for a mate born under Leo, those born between the 5th and the 14th of August are quite a good match. You'll gain a good deal of satisfaction from them.

GEMINI + VIRGO

Air + Earth = Dust

Although both Gemini and Virgo are ruled by the same planet, Mercury, it's an unusual fact that these two star signs don't necessarily see eye to eye.

There is certainly a strong element of communication evident in this match, but the way in which it operates is very different, indeed.

Virgo is critical about every little detail and this will slowly but surely undermine your self-confidence. It's not that you won't have quick and reasonable arguments in response to the demands and criticisms aimed at you, but Virgo could consistently rebut those responses and this will leave you feeling quite exasperated.

The main area in which you will find yourself at odds is domestically. Even if your relationship with Virgo runs smoothly for some time, it will be a different ball game once you spend time with each other in a day-to-day routine. It's here you'll see the maddening position of Virgo driving you wild. From concerns about whether you've washed your hands before dinner to leaving your shoes at a perfect angle, to making sure all the books on the bookshelf are arranged in the correct order of size, will drive you up the wall.

You have a light-hearted and easy manner and enjoy going with the flow for most of the time, but Virgo seems to be more uptight about things. Here's your challenge with them. But, did you know that, if you can relax them, get them laughing and opening up so that their minds are not dominating the circumstances, you'll probably find them much easier to be with? The problem is that these glimpses of a relaxed Virgo may be few and far between. This is also likely to be the case when it comes to your sexual relationship with them. You are free, easy and humorous, whereas they are a little more prudish by your standards.

You have friendly relations with Virgos born between the 24th of August and the 2nd of September because Mercury doubly rules both of you. Your intellectual rapport will be great and although they will chase perfection you'll be happy to let them look after the details. Compromising with them will be hard at times, though.

Virgos born between the 13th and the 23rd of September have a strong Venus influence but this is a co-operative planet and it tells me you could find true love with them. This is a classic combination. These Virgos have a practical approach to life and will be a great asset financially to you.

Virgos born between the 3rd and the 12th of September are spiritually aligned with you and will be wonderful advisers. Maybe you're not looking for a guru in life but you'll certainly feel their words of wisdom will offer you something beyond the day-to-day romance and sexual affair that is so commonplace these days.

GEMINI + LIBRA
Air + Air = Wind

With high levels of imagination, you both tend to live in your minds rather than operating from the heart and this could present problems for you down the track. Although you stimulate each other socially, intellectually and creatively, you need to pay more attention to your emotional connection together.

Socialising is high on your agenda and you both fit in comfortably with each other's friends. There's a touch of magic in the Gemini and Libra relationship and therefore you'd have to say that it's well worth giving this friendship serious consideration. Gemini and Libra are under the air category elementally, which gives you a head start if they choose to enter a relationship with you. This is a very favourable match with the hallmarks of long-term success, but also a few cautionary notes, I should point out.

Air is linked to imagination and communication, so the combination of Gemini and Libra is great for a spirited friendship, if nothing else. Each will stimulate the other and this is excellent socially, romantically and sexually. You'll enjoy entertaining each other and should have a good life with a large circle of friends.

You'll share many similar interests culturally but at times due to your strong mental viewpoints, you will also oppose each other intensely. You are probably wondering when I'd point out the difficulty with this almost-perfect match, right? Well, we all need some challenges and these mental differences can serve to strengthen rather than hinder us if you use the information offered here wisely.

Your lives together may not be so tranquil because you are the types of people who are always on the go, mixing with both your mutual and individual friends. This is an exciting relationship but not necessarily peaceful. Given your open personalities you'll probably learn to live with this.

You stimulate each other sexually as well so it seems that a relationship between the two of you on most counts will get the astrological thumbs up. With your physical energies being triggered by your imagination and fantasies, this could be one area of the match between you that really excels.

I see that an excellent love match is possible with Librans born between the 24th of September and the 3rd of October because Venus, the natural planet of affection, love and marriage has a strong influence over them. Librans born around this time will show their appreciation of your talents and special way of communicating. They'll affectionately show you the love you feel you deserve.

Librans born between the 4th and the 13th of October are electric in nature and are even more changeable than your typical Libran. That's because Uranus and Aquarius, the eccentric sign, dominate them. They hate being pigeonholed and never follow any conservative thinking.

A particularly good combination is with Librans born between the 14th and the 23rd of October. You'll be enamoured by them but mustn't get too overwhelmed. You might feel that you've finally found someone who can offer you stability, but the longer-term view may not be quite so. This match can be a little deceiving.

GEMINI + SCORPIO
Air + Water = Rain

A relationship between Gemini and Scorpio will certainly arouse the curiosity of both of you but may oscillate between a friendship of great promise and one of intense dissatisfaction.

With the Scorpio individual you'll find a deep and sometimes mystical level to them that is hard even for your Gemini mind to fathom. They will certainly test your ability to focus, to concentrate on the deeper aspects of the relationship, and this will be difficult for you. You enjoy the superficiality and casual social aspects of life, while Scorpio demands a deeper commitment from you.

Scorpio is particularly sensitive but also extremely faithful in love. They demand full attention and don't accept compromises from those whom they love. If you have any doubts about this, that doubt will not last for long because Scorpio will bluntly let you know what their expectations are.

Don't try to get around Scorpio with semantics, clever phrases or even humour. It just won't work.

Mind games, although a domain that Scorpio is not afraid to venture into, are not acceptable when it comes to giving their heart to you. You need to understand at the outset that they are all-or-nothing people.

If your Scorpio partner is prepared to open up to you, you'll find your conversations very stimulating. But you mustn't cross them or tear down their ego because they're likely to respond by ripping your ego to complete shreds. As long as you're aware of the sharp and sometimes vengeful aspect of Scorpio, you'll be prepared for those moments when all-out war can emerge between you.

Be prepared also for the fact that Scorpio is possessive, to say the least. Your socialising and free-spirited attitude will be unacceptable to Scorpio once their commitment is given to you.

This may not be a relationship that has enough going for it to make it a lasting one. However, there will most definitely be a high level of energy and interest in each other, and sexually you'll surprise each other, too. With your curious approach to intimate affairs and Scorpio's intense and passionate lust, this could be an area that sustains the relationship a little longer.

You'll find it extremely difficult getting on with Scorpios born between the 24th of October and the 2nd of November. You'll respect each other but your opinions will be worlds apart. You'll try to keep things light and breezy while this Scorpio pulls towards the hot and heavy.

Scorpios born between the 13th and the 22nd of November are very intense, emotional types. This will cause you to feel uncomfortable due to their very deep and serious demeanour.

Those born between the 3rd and the 12th of November are pretty well suited to a lasting relationship or even a professional association. You may meet this Scorpio through a friend at work or some work-related activity.

GEMINI + SAGITTARIUS
Air + Fire = Hot Air

They say that opposites attract and astrologically speaking Gemini and Sagittarius are indeed opposite counterparts. Because of this you do have a natural inclination to want to spend time with each other and your idealism, inspiration and far-sightedness are the beacons of your partnership. These are the characteristics that are common to both of your star signs.

Philosophical yet easygoing, Sagittarius has a slightly different skew on life to the fast and furious Gemini mind. Whereas both of you are flexible, changeable and in need of variety, Sagittarius is not quite as frenetic as Gemini. You are highly strung and nervous. But Sagittarius may well be the catalyst for showing you how to relax a little more in life while at the same time still enjoying everything about it.

You have an intense craving for social life and the company of others and Sagittarius also is not averse to being with others and sharing their experiences. On this note, you'll find much in common. The social context in which you both find yourselves will appeal to you. You like the fact that Sagittarius gets on well with others and travel for the two of you will be a mind-expanding experience, individually and as a couple.

Because your opposite star sign relates to marriage and long-term romantic commitments, you'll both instinctively feel headed in that direction once you commence a relationship together. However, you will constantly need to reassert your closeness and common interests to make this relationship work. With your diverse and sometimes scattered inquisitiveness, it could be very easy for you and your Sagittarian friend to become distracted and thereby lose interest in each other.

Sexually there's quite a good compatibility between the air sign of Gemini and the fire sign of Sagittarius, with both your elements encouraging each other. Communications between you will be enlightening and therefore that can also be used to help stimulate yourselves sexually and emotionally.

I see a good match between you and Sagittarians born between the 23rd of November and the 1st of December. Because of Jupiter's co-rulership, it doubly influences your romantic and marital interests, and this category of Sagittarius is usually generous, both with money and their emotions. At times you might find they are a little wasteful with their resources.

You could hit a brick wall with Sagittarians born between the 2nd and the 11th of December because of their Mars–Aries influence. You'll feel confident that a relationship will work well due to their good conversational style, but this could deteriorate into more of an opinionated attitude that will really annoy the hell out of you. Take stock and listen more than you talk with them.

Those born between the 12th and the 22nd of December are great friends and offer you loads of mental stimulation, good times and support. They'll be there when you need them, carry you through the hard times, and you'll enjoy each other's banter immensely.

GEMINI + CAPRICORN
Air + Earth = Dust

I suggest you think a little more carefully before getting totally involved emotionally with a Capricorn. Why, you ask? It's all a matter of speed. A difference in speed, I mean. Capricorn is a slow, plodding and persevering type of character, whereas you are an individual who lives life at breakneck speed. Are you prepared to keep turning around, wondering how long your Capricorn partner will be in catching up with you? They will also be thinking the same thing. Only in reverse. Their thoughts will be on how to slow you down, how to rein in your wild and zesty energy.

On this basis, the relationship will run into hiccups from day one. This is essentially the problem you're confronted with in a Gemini–Capricorn relationship.

The issues of security are paramount in the mind of Capricorn. Can you offer them the security they are after? This is really at the heart of the Capricorn personality. Their life pursuits are dominated by steadiness, perseverance and the issue of financial satisfaction. You, on the other hand, are free and live life spontaneously. This does not instil too much confidence in your Capricorn partner.

Making a commitment to becoming a more practical person, showing that you want to earn more money and to develop a sense of future finan-cial security will go far in appeasing the concerns Capricorn has about you. You mustn't leave them in doubt as to your sense of priorities in this respect.

There's a strong karmic connection between yourself and Capricorn and this also relates to shared resources and finances. Both of you will have to ask a serious question about what you want out of the relationship and whether or not you're prepared to work persistently and in harmony to find the happy medium.

You know that money is not your primary concern but Capricorn, being a little tight-fisted as they are, will want to take control over these matters and this may cause you considerable uneasiness.

Capricorn is stimulated sexually by you and entertained by your youthful and playful attitude. From time to time, Capricorn will glimpse what it's like to let go of all of the constraints that their personality seems to impose on them. This is the one glimmer of hope that they see in pursuing a long-term relationship with you. Keep it light and breezy but don't forget to pay attention to the issues of security.

Capricorns born between the 23rd of December and the 1st of January are difficult individuals to deal with. Saturn's influence means they are ruthless with money, which will not sit well with you. You are far too free and easygoing for their liking.

Capricorns born between the 2nd and the 10th of January are softer individuals and you'll get on well with them both culturally and creatively. Spending time in mutual interests related to art and culture will help put your relationship on a good footing. These Capricorns can work reasonably well with you.

Capricorns born between the 11th and the 20th of January are more serious than you so it's touch and go with them. Strangely, you'll still feel attracted to them.

GEMINI + AQUARIUS
Air + Air = Wind

All I can say is that the Gemini and Aquarius partnership can be a lot of fun but it is also fairly high maintenance as well.

Wild and progressive Aquarius teaming up with the youthful prankster of the zodiac, Gemini, is a particularly quirky combination that can work, notwithstanding your differences.

When Gemini and Aquarius meet, it's usually in the most ridiculous of circumstances. This will only serve to highlight the unconventional and exciting relationship that is forecast for the two of you. There'll be an intuitive feel about your friendship and one you'll feel is destined from the moment you set eyes upon each other.

Aquarius is a stubborn sort of character and, as you've probably heard, they can be quite rebellious without any particular rhyme or reason. They want to make a point of breaking the rules if only to show you that it can be done. Because of this you'll be attracted to them, and heaven only knows why. Probably because your curious mind likes to try different things.

Your love of variety and interest in intellectual matters intrigues Aquarius and this makes them feel comfortable with you. They are able to discuss their viewpoints and realise that you two have a slightly different perspective on life. They are humanitarian, are social and political, and love to talk about the improvement of the human being as an individual and as a species. You can learn a lot from them and this fascinates you.

Aquarians are innovative and unique as people. The planet Uranus rules them and, although you aspire in some ways to be like them, the abrupt and sometimes unexpected twists and turns in their lives might not be handled all too gracefully by you.

You need to get clarity on their direction and where you fit in the scheme of their lives.

You both have a natural attractiveness about you and this means you love to flirt. This adds spice to your relationship, but the downside is that you may never be able to give each other the commitment you'd like. This is therefore quite an unpredictable arrangement, even if it is a lot of fun. Sexually the same can be expected, for it is both frightening and enticing at the same time.

You have a reasonable chance of enjoying a relationship with Aquarians born between the 21st and the 30th of January. This can be an exciting match because they will push you to exploring new sexual frontiers with them. They are very free with their love and possibly not at all into commitment. This may or may not appeal to you.

You'll feel a very special association with Aquarians born between the 31st of January and the 8th of February. At times it will be as if you're looking into a mirror, seeing yourself in them. They have a good sense of humour and will enjoy an easier-going lifestyle than the typical Aquarian.

You'll be very attracted to Aquarians born between the 9th and the 19th of February. Venus the goddess of love blesses them with not only sensitivity, imagination and artistic talent but also sexual prowess. You'll find a life of romance with them and, if that's what you want, I say go for it.

GEMINI + PISCES
Air + Water = Rain

The first thing to be noted in your relationship with Pisces is their unpredictable and moody nature. The reason for this is their strong connection to the Moon and, as you know, this body revolving around the Earth is the one responsible for the changing tides.

Likewise, you need to be prepared to adjust yourself to the unexpected and often deep and mystical moods of your watery friend.

Pisces lives by an intuitive sense that is instinctive and spontaneous. Certainly Gemini also has spontaneity about it, but you are primarily operating from the level of the head.

You'll find yourself at odds with each other when it comes to making decisions because you prefer the facts and figures while Pisces is happy to rely on intuition and go with the flow.

Both of you have a tendency to run off at tangents. Like the fish that represents Pisces, they are swimming in many different directions all at once. Like the element of air that represents you, it is everywhere all the time, too. This makes it hard for the two of you to anchor the relationship and make it move in one agreed upon direction.

Because Pisces loves people, they are not averse to involving themselves with more than one person at a time. This is probably because of their universal and spiritual approach to life, which tells them that exploring their feelings is one way of evolving spiritually. You also have a need to explore life and, as long as the two of you are on the same page and respectful of the idea of being free to express your love with whomever you want, whenever you want, there shouldn't be too many problems.

Pisces is often deep and brooding and you won't quite know what is going on with them. You like to talk about your feelings and might be confused when Pisces doesn't respond in the way you feel they should. You need to exercise patience and let them speak to you in their own good time. If you take a hands-off approach with them, you're likely to have a far better chance of making the relationship last.

Pisces born between the 20th and the 28th or 29th of February are the most idyllic. If you give them the opportunity they'll take you to a world beyond your wildest dreams, emotionally and sexually. They have uncanny, psychic gifts that allow them to tune into your thoughts and feelings and you'll be amazed how they do it.

Pisces born between the 1st and the 10th of March are quite emotional, sometimes excessively so, and you might not find a relationship with them too fulfilling. They are overly sensitive so you'll be constantly treading on eggshells with them. They could feel offended by your gusto!

Passion is something you seek and Pisceans born between the 11th and the 20th of March will give you as much of it as you can devour. Lovemaking will be great with them but they are fiercely competitive intellectually so you'll have your work cut out for you. The challenge will be worth it!

2010:
The Year Ahead

Time in its ageing course teaches all things.

—Aeschylus

Romance and friendship

There's a real buzz in the air for Gemini in 2010. The presence of the powerful and lucky Jupiter in the upper part of your horoscope as the year starts no doubt promises a most fascinating twelve months ahead. With Neptune in close proximity, your ideals for friendship and love will be strong. You have the power to direct your energies towards fulfilling your personal and romantic ambitions this year. But make no mistake about it: building strong and enduring relationships will take effort, and plenty of it.

Throughout January and February you're intense about creating something magical in your relationships and, if you've been somewhat unlucky in the past, you're destined to turn that around this year. You have energy, ambition and the life force to fulfil your heart's desire. Among one of your strongest characteristics this year is leadership, which will spearhead your success socially and also on the home front.

No longer will you be taking a backseat and, if already in a relationship, you will want to be heard and have strong opinions about what changes need to be made to improve your current love life or marriage. Generally, there are very powerful changes and transformations about to take place, particularly from February through to August. This is due to the very challenging square aspect of Saturn to Pluto and this affects your home life and your most intimate relationships as well. You have to step outside your comfort zone and be prepared to accommodate the changes that life and you yourself will bring to bear in 2010.

Improving relationships is all about looking at yourself in an honest fashion. You'll be prepared to do that to break down the walls of what's been hindering you in getting closer to the one you love, or indeed trying to attract your soulmate. Although this could be a little scary, you mustn't back down as you'll be rewarded with a greater amount of happiness in the long run.

March is an exceptionally good time to increase your circle of friends. Particularly from the second week of this month you will be socialising much more than usual and will even be called upon to act as a mediator to bring opposing parties together. Be careful how you do this, however, as you don't want to appear to be siding with one group or another. Impartiality in your associations will be pivotal.

Venus has the unparalleled reputation of making you attractive and sensual. This is likely to be so in even greater measure after this planet enters your Sun sign around the 25th of April. People will naturally be attracted to you and this is because you'll exude a quiet self-assurance that others will be drawn to. It's also at this time that new relationships can be fostered and true love may be found.

You are rarely afraid to speak your mind but, around this same time, when Mars enters your zone of communications and short travels, you'll be even stronger willed and prepared to stand up for what you believe in. You can make some important inroads into your life and your experience may just clash with others who are not quite as daring as you. On a more familial front, you could have to deal with siblings who oppose you or are envious of your success. You'll need every ounce of diplomacy to handle these emerging situations.

By the time June comes around, it will be very clear to you that sharing power and working towards a mutual relationship is imperative for stability in your life. You'll be interested in sexuality and ways of creating a more intimate and more meaningful rapport with your loved one. This will take considerable effort on your part because if your partner or spouse is not amenable to change you'll have to assert yourself and sell the benefits to them.

If you've attempted this on numerous occasions before, there may be a time coming when you may need to eliminate certain aspects of your life and take this to the extreme. It may or may not work but you'll realise that unless you push as hard as you can, you're not going to get the reaction you are after.

Mars also influences your domestic circumstances throughout June and July and your home environment could change as well. You will not be satisfied with complacency in any way. You'll want your family members, your children and your loved one to get things moving. If there have been issues suppressed and you've been dominated by someone, this is the time to stand up and demand change. This seems to be a recurring theme for you in the coming year.

By the middle of July your home life will be much more harmonious and this again is due to the presence of Venus entering your zone of family life. You'll want to beautify your environment and it could happen that your artistic side will come to the fore in redesigning your surroundings, making your home space much more comfortable. But this could also entail a significant expense, where you'll have to negotiate with others to avoid disputes.

The conjunction of Mars and Saturn in early August is a difficult transit to deal with and requires an immense amount of patience on your part. You may be dealing with the past, enduring hurts or childhood issues that have not been resolved. You will need to make progress at this time and hopefully your nearest and dearest will be a source of strength, not an obstruction to this process. If you can break through some of these patterns of behaviour that have been part of your character for years, you will feel an immense sigh of relief and naturally the start of great new things romantically and emotionally.

Dedicating yourself to your craft or your young-sters in life will take on significant meaning in September and the roles between parent and child may actually be reversed. You will observe many things at this time, which will cause you to relive your childhood and to recall just how much fun it is to live in the moment and not worry too much about things.

Taking this new rejuvenated attitude into your social life will be a blessing and, when your karmic north node enters your zone of marriage around the 7th of September, your quest for a soulmate may be fulfilled to the max. For married couples, a more equal and fair approach to interactions will be evident.

In September and October a sense of responsibility could be amplified, especially if you're in a workplace scenario where you feel drawn to a co-worker. An element of passion and impatience surrounds the combination of Mars and Venus and you are likely to throw your good judgement out the window for the sake of a quick fix, if you know what I mean. Try not to be carried away by the moment, because one-night stands or shallow involvements are likely to take place under these transits.

The Sun impacts upon your life strongly after the 17th of October and, if you haven't scheduled enough time for your own personal relaxation and wellbeing, health may come to the fore as a problem. This is also highlighted by the presence of Mars and Venus in your zone of work and health. You may be excessive in your work practices, working long, hard hours and avoiding your body's signals to rest and eat well.

It's not a bad idea to take up a gym membership during this phase because you'll need something to release the stress of work.

Pay special attention to creativity. You need to reconnect with that part of your nature that is able to produce something other than just money. Look to an older friend who may have gone through similar patterns and has some timely words of advice for you.

The entry of Mars into your zone of marriage and intimate relationships could be problematic for you in November. Whereas you will want more independence, someone may be clipping your wings and demanding that you do things their way. Arguments are likely to develop and your energy will be unmanageable.

Take care with your body and don't overwork yourself throughout November and early December. Mars does have the tendency to cause you to push yourself beyond the limits and injury or strain is likely. Communications are fortuitous in November and any sort of appeal or request for help will be met with a positive response from others. If you've found yourself a little distant from someone you considered a friend, this is the time to rekindle your connection with them.

The final days of 2010 are marked by the energetic planets of Mars and the Sun occupying your zone of public relations and marriage. It's likely you'll feel good about your relationships at this time even though the challenges throughout the year will have pushed some of your buttons. As long as you keep a level head and realise that relationships are bound to be marked by highs and lows, you'll come out of this a much better person and happier, too.

Work and money

During 2010 you have the opportunity to create many new business and professional associations. Between January and March you'll also be able to improve your current situation at work and, if you've had some old gripes with anyone, you're likely to bury the hatchet and move on to improve things generally.

Jupiter creates amazing opportunities for you throughout the year and there will be many opportunities to expand your horizons, commence new work or, within the role you're currently performing, to realise a promotion with the advantage of increased income.

For those of you in an independent line of work, it's likely that a new association will help grow your business enormously at this time.

With the added benefit of Venus entering your professional zone in February, harmonious interactions with your employer or co-workers can be expected, but try not to let your desire for excessive perfectionism make too many demands on others. You don't want to push people too far.

There are some important financial matters that will require you to break out of your routine this year. You may aggressively go after money and an increase of cash flow, but this could be at the expense of your personal relationships. Remember that the best things in life aren't things and that placing too much emphasis on money, power and prestige can erode what you are trying to gain in life, namely love and friendship as well as financial security.

There will be big changes for you between April and July and any frustration you have felt in your work is likely to be expressed explosively. You will need to reassess the direction you are travelling in quietly and not make too many unrealistic demands on yourself. Keep your expectations and your goals realistic. It's not a bad idea to break down your goals into smaller, digestible components so that you won't feel as if the 'big one' is out of reach.

Whatever obstacles stand in your way between May and August can be easily overcome as long as you don't let your frustrations and anger cloud your vision and good judgement. You may be letting your feelings get in the road of your responsibilities and this will cause problems and even more frustration.

Great opportunities, which may unexpectedly appear, are likely between June and September. Although you won't know what's happening from one day to the next, life and in particular your professional circumstances will be full of excitement.

You will again be filled with a high degree of confidence and power in October when Mars and

Jupiter join hands, bringing you some positive outcomes and some brilliantly successful situations. Your competitive spirit will be balanced and therefore you are likely to make new friends and, in the spirit of enterprise, create some new partnerships at this time. Your sales work and your ability to be convincing in an argument will further enhance your opportunities for money and prestige.

Some confusion in November is likely with Mars and Neptune requiring you to assess realistically what you're capable of and what needs to be postponed. Your creative ideas may be met with resistance or you may simply need to grasp what is necessary to make these ideas a reality. If you are dealing with professionals and you are somewhat new to the game, it's best to let others lead rather than putting your own foot forward first. Your foot may just end up in your mouth!

Act decisively to take on that new position in November. Procrastination will only result in bitter disappointment. Sometimes you have to trust your intuition if you want change.

In November and December you'll have the opportunity to fight for a moral or ethical cause and this, although it doesn't seem too related to your work, will certainly be tied in with issues of integrity and honesty. You may be called to set a new benchmark for your peers, so do your best to prove that honesty can coexist with cold, hard business principles.

Your individualism will be marked in the last month of the year and you will have the opportunity to break free of any constraints that have been holding you back. Working along technical, mechanical or engineering lines may be indicated as well. Mathematics and honing your skills at deduction and logic will be important components of making the last part of 2010 a successful one for you professionally.

Karma, luck and meditation

There'll be no shortage of opportunities in every department of life for Gemini-born individuals in 2010. Your incredible confidence will help propel you towards your goals this year and others will take notice of your actions. Jupiter and Pluto provide you with ample opportunities from the early part of February.

During March a new job or promotion brings with it not only an opportunity for increased financial freedom but an enormous amount of self-esteem as well. One point, however: any sort of overconfidence or ostentatious display of your prowess is likely to backfire, so maintain humility and share your good fortune.

Friendships are also part of your good fortune after April, but don't for a minute think that this will be all smooth sailing. To gain the benefits of love and friendship you must also take responsibility and surrender your time and money, perhaps to solidify your connections at this time.

Relationships, marriage and other long-term emotional commitments are favoured by your lucky karma in May and June. Those you once knew in the past who have slipped out of view for some time are likely to re-emerge, bringing joy and possibly even additional career opportunities with them. You should try as hard as possible to reconnect with those extending the hand of friendship, even if you find yourself overworked and too busy. You'll be astounded at what may eventuate as a result.

Extraordinarily lucky times can be expected in August and September. Although you may not have the tendency to gamble, you may win something at this time or be lucky in placing a bet. Lotteries, raffles and other prizes or competitive activities will result in substantial benefits to you.

Romance and affairs of the heart fare well in September with Mars and Venus offering you a good dose of love and lust if you so choose.

In November and December lucky Venus reminds you to take good care of your health, feed yourself well and spend time beautifying yourself outwardly but also inwardly. Meditation, fresh air, an appreciation of nature and other aesthetic activities enhance your life and opportunities. This should be a good year for you to develop your spiritual talents as well as your professional activities.

2010:
Month by Month
Predictions

The future belongs to those who believe in the beauty of their dreams.

—Eleanor Roosevelt

Highlights of the month

Family life and finances are in for a big shake-up in the first month of 2010. Between the 1st and the 8th, you will be actively seeking to create a stronger bond with your family and this will require sensitivity to get everyone on the same page.

Personal growth and progress during this period will be important key words. You will have particularly good relations with those in authority who can help with some of the tedious day-to-day chores associated with your domestic sphere, including council, government and other bureaucracies that are necessary for the smooth functioning of your community.

After the 10th you'll have more time to express yourself in loving relationships. Friendships will also take on a new meaning and you have a stronger urge to get out and participate with others. You'll be carefully evaluating some of your relationships and, when Jupiter lends its hand to the situation, you'll be much more popular but also prone to promise more than you can deliver to someone. Be careful that you can make good your word.

Your career is in the spotlight after the 18th. You can expect a greater satisfaction from your work and not only because you're probably finding yourself earning more money but because you will be able to connect more easily with what you are doing. As a result of this it will be easy for you to ask your boss for a promotion or an additional pay rise.

Travel associated with work, changing jobs and a chance to take on a new study course are all on the cards during this phase of the year. You have the desire to improve your career and to become really good at what you do. If you are in a position for it, you may even be asked to teach or train others as an extension of the role you play in your day-to-day work.

Between the 20th and 25th you will want to reshape your life somehow and therefore gaining a deeper understanding of yourself and the world around you through some philosophical study will also be a possibility. Building a solid foundation upon which you can create not just material but spiritual wealth will be important.

By the 26th your leadership qualities will be duly noted. And, due to the favourable position of Venus, your social and professional lives will overlap and both areas will benefit. Your balanced judgement will be a cause of good fortune and increased positive relations with those around you.

Romance and friendship

Between the 1st and the 6th your mind will be extremely quick but possibly reactive, so make sure you are on your best behaviour. You could lose your cool and will be unaware that someone who really matters is watching your every move.

On the 8th and the 9th you'll be feeling warm and fuzzy and therefore some quiet time with the one you love is probably not a bad idea. You could be averse to socialising with too many people in the evening. Don't feel guilty about it and just enjoy a quiet night at home.

Between the 10th and the 12th you could feel under the weather but will be more on top of your game by about the 15th. You'll emotionally identify with what's happening around you. Try to get more into the flow of loving what you do.

Between the 18th and the 20th you'll have obligations that involve meeting someone face to face. This will encroach on your time but there'll be no way out of it so accept this imposition gracefully. There could be someone on the home front who is demanding your time rather than asking you nicely.

On the 25th a friend could feel that you've been too serious about things and they make an off-the-cuff statement. This should be taken lightly and with a sense of humour. Lighten up or you will run the risk of alienating a friend or two around this period.

On or about the 26th, your mind will be wandering off to far places and you may not be able to keep your concentration level fully on the matters at hand. You could find yourself inattentive to the one you love and daydreaming. You need to get out of your favourite chair, take a deep breath, and re-focus your awareness.

Work and money

You'll be more aggressive about demanding what you want between the 1st and the 4th and may not be able to hold back from letting others know exactly what you want. There's a time and a place for everything and this could shock those with whom you work. You could calm down by the 6th but generally the first week of the month could be rather stormy on the work front.

You could find yourself in an embarrassing situation between the 8th and the 10th and may have to make up the shortfall on a bill. Settling accounts may be troublesome.

Divided loyalties seems to be an issue around the 14th, when making a decision between spending time with someone you love or having a night out on the town with your work colleagues could challenge you. Go with your heart and the person you are romantically attracted to.

Stop postponing meetings with your boss. From the 19th till the 23rd you will need to bite the bullet and deal with several issues. Once you do that you will feel far more relaxed about the fact that it was probably 'a storm in a teacup', anyhow.

Destiny dates

Positive: 15, 21

Negative: 11, 12, 14, 19

Mixed: 1, 2, 3, 4, 5, 6, 7, 8, 9, 10, 18, 20, 21, 22, 23, 25, 26

Highlights of the month

Around the 11th Venus enters your career sector and so your professional associations are smooth and productive this month. You can create positive results in your career. You may have a desire to exercise your authority over others but will be gracious in the way you do it. Perfectionism in all matters will be obvious in your work life.

The Sun entering your most important zone of work on the 19th means you have a gift for expressing yourself in some public arena. Your professional aptitude will be noted by others. Your social status will be on the increase and you'll experience a great sense of achievement throughout most of the month.

Your marital affairs could be bothersome around the 21st. A sense of obligation mars your good feelings with a loved one. You may overstay your welcome somewhere or someone may start to feel weary of your company. You need to be more aware of how others perceive you during this time frame.

Social events will be offered to you but they may be more of a burden than a pleasure. You could resort to overindulgence to handle a socially awkward situation. Don't overdo it and if you have an uneasy feeling before an event it's probably better to make alternative plans rather than playing the martyr to please others.

Your spirit of collaboration resumes a more normal tone after the 23rd. You'll feel better about being with others and have a stronger urge to involve yourself with them. You will make some important observations and evaluations about one or more of your friends at this time and will be most surprised at what you learn.

On the 25th Mars trines the Sun so your cheerfulness and self-confidence will be elevated as the last few days of February are upon you. You will feel poised to attain your goals with greater effortlessness than usual. You will also be prepared to exert yourself physically and won't be averse to a little competitiveness in your work or recreation. Sports will be a good idea to let off steam.

Several meetings will challenge you by the 26th and you are prone to walk away from a situation in which you feel either powerless to do anything or just outright ignored and disrespected. You will want to score a win on your own just to prove a point, but be careful not to create further resistance in others.

You can come to some agreement on the 27th so negotiate the best deal you can for yourself. Trade your ideas with others, but don't give away too much. Someone will be ready to pounce on your concepts to take advantage for themselves.

The bonds of love will strengthen in your romantic or marital life around the 28th. You will feel mutually encouraging and supportive of friends and lovers. If you are new to a friendship or love affair, it is likely that a stronger commitment will take place in this relationship.

Romance and friendship

The 1st and the 2nd are days when you'll want to allow your imagination to run free but unfortunately you might find yourself depressed if your fantasies don't correlate to the reality of your emotional life.

On the 4th, don't pigeonhole yourself by trying to think the way the others want you to. If you meet someone who holds you in contempt for being who you are, you may have to accept the dare and step out of the square, be different and explore what's on offer. You'll thoroughly enjoy these new experiences between the 7th and the 10th.

The 11th and 12th is a sensual cycle and sexuality is strongly spotlighted. You'll have the chance to express how you feel. Stop playing mind games when in a perfect romantic situation. Simply express how you feel because you could miss a beautiful opportunity.

Put aside your idealism after the 18th, at least for the time being, as someone you feel affectionate towards has been placed on a pedestal by you. You must be more objective about this person's real character traits rather than projecting god-like qualities on them.

Follow your intuitive hunches between the 19th and the 21st. Your insights will go a long way to gaining an understanding of your friends and their motivations. It's likely that you'll be able to avoid the ramifications of impulsive love by doing so.

Around the 24th, issues of power and who controls a relationship will be at the forefront. Your personal magnetism may attract unlikely characters who in turn will stir up trouble if you are in a more established relationship.

On the 28th, spend time healing yourself. If your mind and your emotions are in any sort of disorderly state it's the perfect time to reconnect with your inner self and this in turn will help heal your relationships as well.

Work and money

Tension on the work front is caused by the difficult aspects of Saturn and Pluto, but that will ease so don't get bogged down in problems. This will push you out of your comfort zone and it may get more intense before it gets better. It's best to say as little as possible or you may just make things worse between the 1st and the 5th.

You mustn't show your hand on the 7th, even though you may feel guilty for being as shrewd as you will be. This will be the only way to ferret out information and get to the bottom of a situation that's bothering you professionally. You don't necessarily have to be deceptive to be cagey.

The period of the 15th to the 20th shows that you may be holding onto a grudge that will impact upon your work circumstances. You mustn't keep re-visiting past hurts or situations that will only serve to cut short what could otherwise be a long-term and fulfilling relationship with co-workers. Try to see the current situation for what it is rather than relying on your past judgements.

Your business partner or a close working associate may be making excessive demands between the 20th to the 28th. Although you've been pretty good at suppressing your anger, it's likely you'll retaliate over these last few days of February. The situation could escalate between the 26th and the 28th due to the fact that your personal prowess is growing and someone will be envious of you.

Destiny dates

Positive: 3, 5, 11, 12
Negative: 15, 16, 17, 18, 22, 24, 26
Mixed: 1, 2, 4, 7, 19, 20, 21, 23, 25, 27, 28

Highlights of the month

You might feel divided in yourself this month. Around the 3rd internal stress can hamper your efforts to achieve your objectives constructively. Let go of any ego conflicts that arise and use a more diplomatic approach to settling the score with someone. You must try to change your attitude and not carry negative thoughts around with you. Resolve to become strong through any conflicts that arise and try to turn a challenge into an opportunity rather than feeling defeated at the outset.

Between the 4th and the 7th I suggest you give yourself some time out and concentrate on healing your body, mind and emotions. Don't allow a state of chaos to interfere with the smooth functioning of your life. It may be easy to let your daily chores slide and turn a blind eye to less pressing issues, but they will mount up and eventually catch you off guard. Do tomorrow's tasks today and today's immediately.

From the 8th till the 15th you will be particularly popular so don't be surprised if you attract many new friends and admirers during this Venus cycle. The planet of love and friendship will pass though your zone of friends and will certainly bless you with enjoyment and also self-fulfilment. You may also find yourself amid groups of people and could even take on a role of peacemaker or facilitator in the development of some events.

Jupiter will do its thing between the 16th and 20th. As it is a planet given to excess, you need to be watchful not to go overboard. You are likely to go over the top in trying to achieve your ambitions. There is no problem in trying to conquer the world, but learn to accept your limits as well. Your key words will be self-control and temperance.

This is a time when you have opportunities to expand your career choices. It may be that you are offered a new job or a promotion within your current career. You may study or travel in order to expand your professional choices. Whatever the circum-stances you are feeling confident and now is a good time to broaden your professional horizons. Beware of over-confidence, which could lead to taking on too much or making unwise choices. Consider your career prospects and professional responsibilities carefully.

Between the 21st and 30th your main focus will be on your personal dreams. Friends will become a key factor in this, either for good or bad. Discrimina-tion will play a major part in sifting the good from the unhelpful. Pay special attention to the fact that some friends and associates don't really have your best interests at heart and it may be necessary to cut off one or two of them now for your own progress.

Romance and friendship

Between the 1st and the 7th you may have too many irons in the fire. Just remember that the person who does too many things usually has little time to get one thing done properly. You may be giving the nod to too many social engagements, so the best advice is to focus on the one thing, or rather the one person you feel closest to, and put aside other social distractions for the time being.

Don't lead-on people on the 8th. Even if you feel the flattery is quite comforting, you should be honest as this will win you respect and also make life less complicated. On the 10th it's likely you'll win the approval of several people and may find it difficult to choose between them.

A friend's behaviour on the 12th and 13th could leave you speechless and confused as to how to deal with them. You'll probably be feeling more tradi-tional in your ways and will be at a loss to explain their rather radical or unexpected behaviour. Try not to judge them too harshly because there's probably more to the situation than meets the eye.

Your love life could be quite compulsive between the 15th and the 18th. You'll attract many new friends and will have the chance to socialise consid-erably, but one person may take your eye and you may not be able to get them out of your mind.

You'll need to assert yourself more strongly between the 18th and the 20th. If you're trying to please everyone all the time, you'll never get to say your piece. A show of power or control may be what is necessary to gain the attention of someone important.

You should anticipate a bout of lethargy between the 26th and the 28th. But don't fall asleep or you may miss the most important and tantalising aspects of some social news. Pay more attention to what's being said and get adequate rest beforehand if possible.

Work and money

Your mind will be on all things financial this month, especially between the 3rd and the 10th. If you've been slack in saving your pennies, you may now regret it. In any case, you will make a decision to improve yourself financially and to look after your future security more carefully. It could be difficult for you to develop new habits but the best time to start something is now.

The gloss will be wearing off a particular job you've been doing and, if the money is not quite what you'd like it to be, you may need to elaborate on some new terms of agreement. Arguments over these issues may arise around the 17th and it's best to approach your employer in a mode of humility rather than aggression.

You could be placed in a confusing situation where your ethics or morals are challenged on the 30th. It's not that you are a bad person, but there may be a situation that doesn't fit any particular past experience you've had, and you'll just have to play your cards as you're dealt them. Don't be afraid of making a mistake because errors are the way you will grow in life.

Destiny dates

Positive: 11, 14, 21, 22, 23, 24, 25, 29

Negative: 1, 2

Mixed: 3, 4, 5, 6, 7, 8, 9, 10, 12, 13, 15, 16, 17, 18, 19, 20, 26, 27, 28, 30

Highlights of the month

Between the 2nd and the 7th, your relationship may go through an important change. You will grow much closer to your lover in this period and this is because you feel a common bond with each other. Your interests together will deepen your union. You will feel extremely happy in your love life.

If, on the other hand, you've started a new relationship, the situation will escalate and bring you into a more serious affair. Even if previously you've only considered this person as a friend, you'll be surprised at how quickly your feelings for each other will accelerate.

Your partner or spouse will be fully supportive of your career and your professional activities in this period. Between the 5th and the 10th of April, there'll be a more co-operative state of affairs on the home front that will help you in your plans, giving you more confidence and a sense of stability.

Between the 8th and the 15th, however, when

Mercury transits your low-key zone of self-reflection, you'll spend more time away from the public eye studying your inner self and will be less inclined to make a connection with the world at large. It will be as if you're in a cocoon waiting to emerge from your hibernation, and when you do you'll experience a new surge of energy—a new lease of life to tackle projects and other work-related assignments.

Around the 16th, you'll have an interest in social interactions and your diplomatic charm will attract many new friends to you. There is the possibility of being a little too outspoken, so be careful not to rub up people the wrong way.

With Venus moving through your career zone in the period of the 18th to the 24th, you'll have a perfect opportunity to use your personal contacts to further your professional ambitions. It's likely your superiors will want to include you in meetings or other events from which you'd normally be excluded. Making great friends and forging new business contacts will help you grow your business, increase your bank balance, and also enhance your public reputations.

One of the key issues between the 25th and the 27th may be whether or not you can take care of your family responsibilities. It's not that you don't have the financial ability to do so nor the desire; work commitments may take you out of the loop and this could cause some anxiety for you. You could find yourself between a rock and a hard place trying to please employers on the one hand and family members on the other. It could be a case of divided loyalties at this time.

It won't matter what choice you make because at some point the other party may not be satisfied with the decision you make. As the old saying goes, 'you can't please everyone all of the time'.

Romance and friendship

Perhaps your ideals in love haven't been as high as they could be. You need to step up and create a better romantic life for yourself by expecting better. Between the 3rd and the 5th you can use your creative visualisation to improve your situation. Think about what you want rather than dwelling on what you don't have.

You'll have the opportunity to step out and off the treadmill around the 12th to the 14th. Even if this costs you in lost wages, it's well worth taking the time to travel and improve your health, vitality and perception of the world.

You need to be wary of the smoke and mirrors that someone may be utilising in their negotiations with you around the 18th. You are receptive to others' impressions, but are these impressions true? Don't be taken for a ride.

Between the 18th and the 24th a mini re-shuffle may be necessary in your home if you're planning to take in a guest or a visitor. They may overstay their welcome, however. Get some savvy on their plan beforehand.

Around the 27th you'll be more factual about your feelings rather than letting your emotions colour your decisions. If you let your heart rule your head you could find yourself in an embarrassing situation that will be difficult to reverse.

Pay special attention to your health and your fitness on the 30th. In particular, take note of your eyesight because reading under dim lights or straining your eyes late at night may be the cause of diminished vision. Don't forget to increase your vitamin intake, as this will also help extend your lifespan and give you the energy you need to relate to people in a better manner.

Work and money

Between the 2nd and the 6th you'll have to get into the flow of the group mentality. It may be hard to think along the same lines as your peer group because some of their ways and mannerisms will seem odd to you. For a few days, use this as a period of experimentation to see how the other half thinks and works.

The energies around you between the 12th and the 14th are explosive but you need to redirect yours in a way that is not confrontational or damaging to your reputation. You can still achieve the same results without being overly bossy to your subordinates. Someone you work with may have a complaint against you.

You'll be very focused on your work after the 24th and work matters in particular should go

smoothly because of your heightened concentration and your charm. Try to turn off from work when
pleasure comes knocking at your door, however.
Don't overdo it.

The 29th and 30th are lucky days but you need to
put yourself in the right situation to capitalise upon
this fact. The planets will be bringing you several
opportunities and the doors will open up wide for
you. A new job opportunity is very promising.

Destiny dates

Positive: 7, 8, 9, 10, 11, 15, 16, 29

Negative: 25, 26, 27

Mixed: 2, 3, 4, 5, 6, 12, 13, 14, 18, 19, 20, 21, 22, 23,
24, 30

Highlights of the month

There's a serious tone to your horoscope through-out the period of May and this is due to the fact that Saturn is edging its way backwards through your domestic sphere. From the 1st till the 10th, you'll want to pay special attention to what's happening with loved ones, relatives and other people you associate with on a more intimate level.

The Moon and Venus spotlight your interactions in long-term personal relationships. Due to the influence of Saturn, you will want to break down the status quo and start afresh with an emotional 'spring cleaning'.

With Mars also powerfully influencing your third zone of communications, you will be completely forthright with what you have to say and this could shock others because you are normally more measured in your speech—or at least more cautious about not offending others.

Between the 13th and the 15th, Mars will make a favourable aspect to the Sun, showing that your high energy levels will contribute to your accomplishments and you'll be able to do this quite easily. You may feel as if you're leaving others behind because your initiatives may not take into account the pace at which they wish to move. In any case, this two- or three-day window of opportunity indicates that you can be successful at whatever you put your hand to.

Around the 20th, the bright and uplifting Sun moves into your birth sign of Gemini, assuring you of an extra dose of confidence and attractiveness. You are impressive, to say the least, and you should take the time to capitalise on this powerful surge of energy that gives you success in any sort of meeting to do with the public, a job application or a competitive scenario where you are trying to outwit someone else. It will be pretty hard not to notice you in the last few days of May.

Between the 25th and the 31st, take note that you should not suppress your feelings, even if you think you may unsettle someone. Mars will make contact with your zone of secrets and it's up to you to reveal what you know, even if telling the truth can be a little painful.

During the latter part of the month, you may also be called upon to assist in someone's difficult situation. They may be either unwell or struggling financially. Your advice would be the best way you could help them, but be warned: you must not part with money because this could complicate your relationship with them.

Romance and friendship

Let bygones be bygones on the 1st and the 2nd and don't go dredging up the past. You could be holding onto a grudge or vice versa—someone in your family may be doing the same. If this is a family matter it's best to leave it alone and simply maintain the peace. No good will come out of it otherwise.

You may have forgotten some of your best talents in the bedroom but have the opportunity to revive them on the 8th. Think back to a time when your power was at its peak, and if you are feeling run down, low in spirits or inhibited in your relationships, recollecting the past will be of great value to you.

Don't be afraid to ask for what you want in your relationship on the 18th. It's time for you to receive your 'just desserts'. Why not make that appointment with the person of your dreams and ask them the big question? Be reasonable in your demands and the response should be equally reasonable.

Intense social activities around the 20th stimulate you but also keep you guessing about the intentions of someone you may meet. Your life is filled with unconventional or unexpected twists and turns. Your feelings will be rather unstable, but this is still an exciting period.

You will be carefully evaluating your feelings for someone around the 27th. You want to express how you feel and participate in their life more actively. You can't force yourself on them, so wait for the invitation. It's likely to happen at any time.

You may overlook a kind gesture on the 29th and perhaps wonder why you are not being taken more notice of. Look more carefully: you may discover a note, message or other gesture of love that had previously passed by your attention.

Work and money

Delegating your tasks between the 6th and the 8th will be important and you should avail yourself of the help that is offered if you have the opportunity. This will free up an immense amount of time and give you the chance to do what you do best.

If you're at home, you need to put your foot down and demand that others play their part in contributing to the household chores around the 12th. You can't do everything yourself.

If you continually repeat the words 'I can't do it', the likely outcome is that nothing will get done! Between the 15th and the 20th, even if you feel confronted by challenges and don't feel confident enough in your expertise, use your mind powers to spur yourself on and repeat to yourself 'I can do it; I can do it'. Try it to see what happens. You'll be absolutely amazed at how you will be more capable than you ever thought you were.

Re-establishing your values after the 25th will take on a more important focus for you. It's best to do that before any unexpected twists of fate take you by surprise.

Destiny dates

Positive: 13, 14, 15, 18, 20
Negative: 1, 2, 3, 4, 5, 9, 10, 12, 26, 28, 29, 30, 31
Mixed: 6, 7, 8, 25, 27

Highlights of the month

This is an important time of the year when the all-powerful Jupiter commences its move out of your career sector. Your focus will be changing towards friendships and other alliances. Even if your mind is deeply entrenched in the work at hand, you'll realise the significance of partnerships in work-related relationships and how they are going to hold you in good stead in the future.

The exchanges you have with your work associates will be telling on your productivity. You realise too that 'no person is an island unto themselves' and that the input of your friends, their help, and their backing of you in all the little things you do, means they're certainly the building blocks of your own success. This will become very evident around the 4th of the month when certain other astrological factors cause you to revise your plan for your business procedures.

Jupiter will come in contact with abrupt and

electric Uranus in this month. This may mean not just a revision of your work but a complete change that is thrust upon you from out of the blue. If you're not prepared for these changes, you might find yourself panicking a little. As the old Boy Scouts' motto says, you must 'be prepared'.

Between the 6th and the 10th, unpredictable Uranus will make itself felt for many Gemini-born natives. What this means is that you'll be tested. You could be frustrated in many areas of your life and the challenge for you will be to exercise patience amid circumstances that could seem tedious, demanding and often at times not at all fulfilling.

As a result of this sudden influence, a secondary push by the Sun around the 21st will cause you to take a greater interest in your finances, your possessions and your material attitudes generally. If you've been rather extravagant with your money, you'll find that this is a time for you to tighten your belt and be less of a spendthrift. This will be hard, however, because Venus will also be luxuriously prodding you to spend, spend and spend just a little more.

Around the 27th, you will come to realise you have very little control over others, especially family members. Try not to upset yourself over the belief systems or the actions and lifestyles of someone you love. Give them your best advice; but the bottom line is that they need to live their lives on their own terms and learn from the experiences that are coming to them. There's nothing really much more you can do about that.

Romance and friendship

Due to the return of the Sun to your Sun sign of Gemini you'll be feeling more up-beat, probably for the first time in a while and, between the 2nd and the 4th, several social meetings will make you feel better about yourself and more on top of things generally. Use this positive energy to improve your relationships and at the same time don't forget to exercise your physical body to capitalise on this positive cycle. This should be a refreshing few days for you.

You may be indecisive about changing your wardrobe around the 5th but you mustn't be afraid to step out on a limb and try different styles and colours, even if at first you feel that this doesn't particularly suit your usual character.

By the 10th, you'll be astounded at the difference your efforts can make, both for your own wellbeing and also the way others perceive you. This will definitely keep others on their toes and make yourself the centre of attention for a while, if that's what you want.

Between the 15th and 17th you could be overly stimulated in your feelings. Your excessive lifestyle requires a balance of quiet time and leisure.

Organising your diary will be the name of the game on the 21st and 22nd. Be diligent with your timetable, punctual with your engagements and also clear and concise about expressing your thoughts and feelings to your friends and loved ones.

Surprising news between the 22nd and the 24th exposes you to ideas and information that may challenge your internal status quo. You'll be tested inasmuch as you'll have to either accept or reject a friend or two.

Work and money

After the 3rd, your imagination may be completely out of control. Stop projecting your fears and enjoy what you do. What you perceive is completely at odds with the reality of the situation.

You'll be working extremely hard and maybe pushing yourself to the limits after the 10th. Punishing yourself with exceedingly long work hours boils down to a basic mistrust of your own integrity and abilities. Relax and try to enjoy your work.

Between the 18th and 22nd, you'll need to check your money at the time of a transaction, otherwise there's no hope of gaining a later refund. In haste, you may overlook just how much you've paid someone.

Don't be so charitable on the 24th. The person you hand your money over to may not exactly be in need.

Between the 27th and the 30th you need to focus on the fact that work must be in keeping with your personality and in-built talents. If you're feeling that this is not the case, it may be time for you to look further afield and try something new. If you've settled into the security trap, this could be difficult.

Be prepared to take a chance, especially if a new opportunity is presented to you.

Destiny dates

Positive: 2, 4

Negative: 6, 7, 8, 9, 18, 19, 20, 24

Mixed: 3, 5, 10, 15, 16, 17, 21, 22, 27, 28, 29, 30

Highlights of the month

The Sun and Mercury interact with the intense and transformative Pluto throughout the month so it's essential to see the big picture when dealing with money. Between the 1st and the 5th, issues relating to sexuality, shared resources and finances generally will be significantly focused in your life. These will be matters at the top of your agenda.

The growing proximity of Saturn to Mars is a further challenge this month and warns that you need adequate, constructive outlets to channel the frustrating influence of Saturn, which may be still lingering from the previous month. Anger, passive aggression and other debilitating emotional states are quite likely under these transits and need to be monitored and dealt with promptly.

Between the 12th and the 15th, you can cushion the impact of these difficult planetary transits by making life more comfortable for others rather than more difficult. By reaching out, going the extra mile to make a situation easier for someone else, your actions will prove to be an emotional investment. Others are more likely to respond in a kind and helpful fashion if they see this reflecting in you.

Around the 16th, you can be decisive although a little headstrong in making some decisions for the family or your peer group, particularly if they have been procrastinating and are unable to make up their minds about something. Arm yourself with the correct information because you will need to be very convincing, almost like a sales rep, if you're to get others on board.

Around the 20th, you'll receive some news that will distract you from the job at hand and cause you to have to fly off at a tangent when you can ill afford the time. You will again be reassessing your position in many areas of life; the key point here is to not force anyone's hand and under no circumstances sign contracts until you've had a second legal or accounting opinion to back up your actions.

After the 22nd, there's plenty of scope for short journeys or field trips and these may well be associated with your professional activities. Your business life will be hectic so make sure your diary is in order. Planning more effectively will become essential and you'll realise some gaping holes in the way you've been approaching your professional efficiency.

From the 25th till the 30th, you'll feel a much stronger sense of appreciation for that which is beautiful in life. You'll have a keener appreciation for art, music and other aesthetic pastimes. This is a good time of the month to take time out and share these feelings with someone of like mind.

Romance and friendship

Between the 1st and the 5th, your friendships requiring a collaborative input will prosper. However, you could find yourself being smothered by friends who are using you. You will be able to see what's going on, but your inability to stand up for yourself will be rooted in your insecurity and you may lose a friend. Don't allow others to use, or rather, abuse you.

Between the 7th and the 8th you'll be somewhat obsessive about someone you meet. You could be coming on too strong and completely oblivious to what another person's intentions are. This might cause you to act inappropriately.

Sudden and exciting love affairs seldom last but the situation between the 9th and the 15th is different. You have a rare opportunity to meet someone who sweeps you off your feet when you least expect it.

You'll enjoy the attention you receive between the 19th and the 23rd; but will you be able to juggle so many demands, both socially and professionally? You may need to get a 'social secretary' to handle this!

You need to open your heart to the concept of sharing and pay someone fairly around the 26th. If someone's done a good job for you, given you their time and shared many of their own inner secrets, it would unfair of you to hold back. Karma will bring you benefits by reciprocating and, as you know, the saying 'what goes around, comes around' may be quite applicable at this point in time.

Between the 28th and the 30th the hot and sexual planet Mars will cause you to be much more romantic but also sexually active. You'll have ample opportunity to express yourself physically and this may be with someone whom you are currently involved or perhaps even a perfect stranger.

Work and money

On the 2nd, there's no point holding back even if you think your words are going to upset the status quo in your workplace. Communicating to superiors will be spotlighted and what you have to say will have some bearing on the outcome of a situation.

Expect a hectic schedule between the 6th and the 14th. The stressful pace at which you'll be operating may involve a tremendous amount of information that has to be digested. Try to stay in your lane as you could end up stepping on other people's toes.

With the influence of Mars and Saturn causing you to feel some frustrations, the dates of the 17th to the 25th will cause you to feel blocked. The secret is to overcome resistance and don't challenge others on too many minor details. Friction will result if you don't quietly accept what life has in store for you.

You can make some great business and social contacts between the 25th and the 27th. Don't forget to ask for one of those business cards being handed out, because you'll need it down the track.

Destiny dates

Positive: 15, 16, 25, 27, 28, 29, 30

Negative: 6, 7, 8, 17, 18, 24, 25

Mixed: 1, 2, 3, 4, 5, 9, 10, 11, 12, 13, 14, 19, 20, 21, 22, 23, 26

Highlights of the month

Between the 1st and the 5th, you will be busy if not somewhat stressed, making plenty of calls and taking on others' responsibilities, particularly in a social context. As a result of taking on more than you can handle, you could find yourself in one or more confrontational situations with those around you. Try to balance your time and be realistic about what you can and can't achieve.

From the 6th till the 12th, your self-image will be all important and you may go to great lengths by spending money trying to become something you aren't. This is a cycle in which you'll be trying to keep up with the Jones's; looking at others to determine your fashion statement. Be true to yourself.

Your creative impulses are further amplified by the presence of Venus in your zone of creativity through the whole of August, but in particular after the 20th. It's the perfect time to join an art class or get back into a handicraft hobby or some musical pastime that has previously given you a lot of fulfilment. You can expect an increased interest in cultural events and activities as well and, if this involves your partner or spouse, it will be an excellent way of generating more love between you.

After the 16th, you'll want something new in your life and your energy will be very spontaneous and restless. You'll openly seek people from different walks of life who hold very different views to the norm. This is a period where your choice of friends may be at odds with what others expect from you, but this won't bother you because it will feel right.

As far as deeper emotional ties are concerned, some born under Gemini may find themselves attracted to unusual people, possibly even from different cultures. Sudden encounters with members of the opposite sex are exciting and very freeing. If you've felt blocked in a current relationship, you might need someone who radically alters you view of where you are on your path in life and even might opt to end the relationship for the promise of a more exciting and fulfilling alternative.

From the 20th to the 30th, there are some important changes that you will implement in your work and these revolve around the technology and mechanics of how you do your work and the instruments or machinery that comprise your professional activities.

The planet Uranus hints at a steep learning curve at this time. If you're unaware of certain technical processes, this is the time to take a supplementary course and put yourself more clearly in the picture of where the world is heading. This will be a cycle where you'll be in discussions with your employers on these very matters and they may agree to supplement your income by paying for a study course and improving your skills as part of your job.

Romance and friendship

From the 1st till the 4th, some of your indiscretions may be highlighted. Someone could reveal your shortcomings and this can either be taken in the proper way as a means of improving your character and spirituality, or possibly as an insult. The choice is yours.

Venus moves to your zone of romance on the 7th so expect your love life to pick up pace at this time. On the other hand, someone who's been annoying you and constantly on your case may disappear for a while or, better still, permanently. This will mean you'll experience more peace and certainly be more in control of your environment generally.

Around the 10th, your quick-witted responses will get you out of a pickle. You mustn't be afraid to say what's on your mind and to do it in a way that catches the other person off guard. You'll get the upper hand and will surprisingly gain the respect that should be afforded you. Once you've made your point, however, let it go. You don't need to get into the humiliation game.

Between the 11th and the 14th, your relationships may be cool and withdrawn. You and your partner are likely to be very reactive during this couple of days and you'll need to take a backseat and simply play the spectator game. Let your friends and lovers feel in whatever way they want to feel and not force any issue. This cycle will pass soon enough and will give you a chance to reappraise the direction of your relationship.

Mercury moves into retrograde motion around the 21st and, on the 23rd, the Sun moves into your zone of domestic affairs. You may change your mind on some matter—possibly an expenditure or event that was supposed to take place within the family circle. Postpone this until you feel more comfortable.

Work and money

New clients, customers and other avenues of earning money are obvious to you from the 1st. The combination of the Moon, Jupiter and Uranus in your zone of social affairs and profitability means you can combine your work and your social life in an excellent manner and thereby be quite profitable.

Working behind the scenes is in order between the 3rd and the 6th. Stay out of the road of others who are antagonistic and also opposed to your methods of doing things. You'll know best and can shortcut your way to improve profitability and deadlines by going it alone.

Minor physical problems between the 12th and the 16th will put you out of action for a while. These are not serious but you do need to address them, otherwise these niggling aches and pains will slow your progress.

A busy few days can be expected from the 21st to the 26th; but note that Mercury being retrograde means that you'll be chasing your tail and not quite able to tie up the deal or get the answers you're looking for.

Enjoy the leisurely stroll through your local mall but be realistic about what you can afford on the 28th.

Destiny dates

Positive: 27, 29, 30

Negative: 2, 13, 14, 15

Mixed: 1, 3, 4, 5, 6, 7, 8, 9, 10, 11, 12, 16, 20, 21, 22, 23, 24, 25, 26, 28

SEPTEMBER

Highlights of the month

You are considerably more emotional this month, as shown by the presence of the Moon in your Sun sign as September commences. The hard aspects to the Sun and Mercury also reveal a certain confusion surrounding your self-image and what others want from you, particularly between the 1st and the 7th.

With the combined influence of Venus and Mars in your zone of personal love affairs, your passions could make you blind to the expectations of your peer group or family members. Under these transits, you may want love and a relationship but may have to sacrifice something in return by going against the approval of others.

Nevertheless, you are caring and loving and are able to generate empathy from at least some of the supporters for your cause.

If you missed some valuable opportunities earlier in the year, the retrogressive dance of Jupiter through your career sector again means you have a second bite at the cherry after the 12th. You can advance your career and this is likely because of your diligent and persistent work ethic. You might have felt that you'd been overlooked; but won't you be surprised when you're rediscovered and the contributions you've made become appreciated! This is going to instil a great deal more faith in your abilities and will of course help you in achieving your lifelong dreams. This is a stepping stone to bigger and better things.

Between the 13th and the 19th, there is likely to be some visible friction in your workplace. Your co-workers may be pushy and demanding, or vice versa. Perhaps this may be the case on both sides of the fence, which will exacerbate a problem. If you're feeling as if you're still not being appreciated, you may be impulsive enough to walk off the job and attempt something new. However, don't 'jump out of the pan and into the fire' before you check all options that are available, or you may just leave yourself out in the cold.

You'll be making greater efforts in relationships between the 22nd and the 24th and the relationship between Saturn and Pluto, albeit a difficult one, does loosen your grip on the past making it easier to throw off those things that are hindering you. You may come to learn of the past cause of behavioural patterns in your lover or a friend. Previously you may not have understood why they were behaving in the way they do. This will be a tremendous break-through, bringing you closer together.

From the 25th till the 30th, the energising and inspiring energies of the Sun touch your spirit and those of the youngsters in your life. Reconnecting with your children if you're a parent is an important component of this cycle. Speaking more openly about your feelings will be reciprocated and you can expect better relations with young people all around as September draws to a close.

Romance and friendship

You're in two minds and possibly confused about where you should live and put your roots down between the 1st and the 8th. You are your own worst enemy at this time and if you can't find the solution quickly enough, it's best to let it slide for a while until the universe provides you a few more hints as to the proper course of action.

You should despise the free lunch around the 15th. Someone has an ulterior motive if they're offering you lunch, favours and other benefits that they normally wouldn't. You should treat these gestures with considerable suspicion.

Your social life can be challenging and also inspiring on the 21st but you'll need to ask yourself where to direct your energies most effectively. There may be several different groups of people that seem appealing to you but you'll need to make choices now to utilise your time well and to feel comfortable in the company of those people.

Relationships are never static and you realise this on the 23rd when the Sun enters your zone of romance. You'll be forced to adapt your character yet again to the person you love or a friend that you wish to keep close. You could think that their demands are over the top but at the end of the day these changes are for your personal growth and greater welfare.

Between the 26th and the 30th, that radical change in your domestic situation may not be able to be postponed any longer. You may have instigated the overhaul, which will now cost you more than you had expected. Re-think the benefits rather than dwell on the downside. Whatever it is you've chosen to do, it will have a marked impact on your family, but try to expect the best, anyhow.

Work and money

Dealing with an older male figure, probably your boss, will be unavoidable between the 1st and the 5th. You could feel as though you're being singled out among your peers. You're far more skilled in your work and therefore a larger responsibility will be placed on your shoulders. Take this as a compliment!

Things can and do change between the 9th and the 14th on the work front. Firstly, Venus brings its graceful charm to your work location, giving you a greater sense of ease and comfort with those whom you work and the environment you happen to be placed in.

Taking a calculated risk between the 19th and the 21st is not a bad idea, as long as you're armed with all the information to do it. This may not necessarily have to do with gambling per se but if you're thinking of moving onto greener pastures and something's offered, it's well worth investigating and even taking the plunge.

Investments pay handsomely from the 23rd to the 25th. If you have a stock market portfolio or other long-term investments you're likely to see an increase in their value. For novices in this arena, it could be well worth your time to look into how you too can capitalise on these long-term strategies.

Destiny dates

Positive: 9, 10, 11, 12, 20, 21, 22, 24, 25
Negative: 1, 2, 3, 4, 5, 6, 7, 8, 15, 16, 17, 18
Mixed: 13, 14, 19, 23, 26, 27, 28, 29, 30

Highlights of the month

You sometimes have to be cruel to be kind and in the case of older family members this will be obvious this month. Someone may not be listening to you and it may be time for you to take full control and handle the matter once and for all. This is likely between the 3rd and the 7th when the people around you are not really seeing what needs to be done. You may seem like the cruel and heartless individual in the scenario but you will eventually be thanked for taking the helm of the ship and steering it to a safe harbour.

A more entertaining and fun time can be expected from the 10th till the 15th. Plenty of entertainment is on the cards with parties and other social events cramming your diary. It's also likely you'll feel more zest and vigour for life and will find yourself in the midst of a younger group of people. There may be the possibility of meeting someone who can help further your creative interests or some work project.

After the 20th, your organisational skills and discipline will pick up and your employer may temporarily give you the opportunity to prove just how capable you are in a more senior role in your work.

You've come through some of the earlier challenges of the year and have dedicated yourself to a sustained effort that will now make life much easier for you. This is a strengthening time and one in which your confidence emerges even more strongly.

By the 26th, a discussion you have with someone may open your eyes as to the cause of some lingering health concern that you had. At first, you may not clearly relate the causes with the symptoms but deeper reflection will prove this person correct. By knowing what the issue is or, more importantly, what the causes are, you can eliminate those from your life and look forward to improved health and vitality.

Between the 27th and the 31st, you must make sure that all your communications are checked and rechecked. Spelling or grammatical errors may result in misunderstandings that can cost you financially. Double-check your meeting times or places of engagement, as sudden changes in plan may be overlooked or not conveyed to one or other parties. Keep your communication consistent and try not to let minor irritations get the better of you.

Romance and friendship

Between the 1st and the 4th, you may end up on a blind date or meeting someone who is interested in you but you may not feel quite comfortable enough to share your feelings with them. Remain calm, cool and collected in the way you express yourself. There's no need to reach the finishing line yesterday.

If you've been feeling as if you're under the thumb of someone, dominated and not quite in control of your own life, the period of the 10th till the 15th is an important cycle in which you can assert yourself again and finally break free of that person. It's time to live on your terms.

It will be time to resume a hobby that you'd put to the side a while ago, but to do so means a sacrifice in some other area of your life. Put aside your duties, share the load with some of the other family members, and dare to resume your passion and love. This can take place between the 19th and the 22nd.

If travel is something that you've also postponed, you might like to pull out those brochures and make some enquiries as to some interesting worldwide destinations. By the 25th you'll have your eye and your heart set on somewhere exotic, romantic and well within the reach of your budget.

Mars enters your zone of marriage and partnerships on the 28th, bringing with it a dose of spice, if not contention.

Smooth relations and great communications take place around the 29th till the 31st of October. You'll find yourself in the company of some beautiful people who will also make you feel equally as wonderful.

Work and money

Discussions are intense and profuse around the 3rd and the 4th. You may make a point but, particularly if you're involved in public relations or a sales-oriented business, you might actually lose the customer rather than convincing them of your viewpoint. Try to say less and you'll have a better chance of sealing up the deal.

You'll be able to curtail your expenses between the 8th and the 15th. Venus moves into retrogression so this is actually a great period to learn from your past errors and become more frugal with your finances.

Take the pressure off by enjoying yourself at work around the 19th and 20th. You can feel inspired and bring a touch of creativity, art and even music into your work place. This will soothe your frazzled nerves and make you far more productive.

New techniques and systems for improving things generally in your professional life take place between the 21st and the 24th. There may be consultants or other trainers brought in to help you learn new methodologies. Education for the purposes of improving your professional abilities and communication skills will be plentiful up till the 27th.

The comments of a work colleague or client will inspire you around the 28th. Take their advice.

Destiny dates

Positive: 8, 9, 19, 20, 21, 22, 23, 24, 25, 26

Negative: 5, 6, 7, 27

Mixed: 1, 2, 3, 4, 10, 11, 12, 13, 14, 15, 28, 29, 30, 31

NOVEMBER

Highlights of the month

No less than four planets are retrograde, meaning they're going over old ground in many areas of your life. This is necessary to make sure that the decisions you are contemplating are not based on false assumptions or faulty knowledge. In particular, Mars moving through your zone of marriage and public relations indicates that it is worth your while to double-check everything before opening your mouth. Mars is prone to misunderstandings and your relationships can take on a more competitive or aggressive edge during this phase of the year.

From the 1st till the 5th, there may be some power struggle; a desire for one of you to dominate the other in your personal life. Unless compromises are reached, this could be a difficult time that will cause your blood to boil over.

A romantic attachment is likely to arise in your workplace or with someone you least expect this month. The period of the 9th till the 15th of November is particularly highlighted for these matters. You need to be clear in your intentions and also ask the other person to state their case. Initially, this may all be guesswork and superimposing of your feelings on each other. This could make it awfully difficult to work, with your concentration levels being deluded by the distraction of loving eyes staring at you from the far corner of the office. Yes, it's best to get things straight and make sure that your romantic feelings for a co-worker don't interfere with your productivity or, worse still, your reputation.

Between the 21st and the 24th, you will react a little too hastily and thereby need to retract your statements. If you're working in the capacity of an advisor, counselling others or mediating between opposing parties, this will take on even greater significance because what you say will affect their decisions.

There are times when fashion and self-beauty can be taken to the extreme; the period of the 27th till the 30th is one such time. Some of you may have contemplated cosmetic surgery or procedures that are rather radical in the hope of making yourself look younger and more appealing. By all means do it but, in repeating the advice I've given in several predictions this year, I say please get a second opinion and additional advice before going ahead.

Romance and friendship

There's something discomforting about someone who tries too hard in love. You mustn't make too many attempts or smother your partner because desperation is the last thing a prospective lover will be attracted to between the 2nd and the 5th.

Are you still trying to keep up with friends in the lifestyle department? This may be a recurring theme this year. That's not a good idea and, in fact, it's a sure path to depression if they keep one-upping you. Between the 5th and the 10th, try to remain content within yourself and the circumstances you happen to be in your life. That's a challenge, but challenge enough. This attitude of mind will bring you more happiness than the designer label outfit your friend is wearing.

You're constructive in working through relationship issues between the 16th and the 18th. Try to be realistic about what you expect from another person and if the demands for improvement require a lot of work, why not break these down into digestible parts so that your counterpart can actually achieve what is expected of them? If you demand too much change too soon it won't happen at all.

You'll quite likely catch someone out in a white lie sometime around the 21st. Some secrets will be revealed and it may take a delicate balancing act to maintain cordial relations with them and the third parties involved. Is any of this your business, anyhow? Don't complicate the issue by sharing this information with anyone else. You could be branded a gossipmonger.

Between the 22nd and the 28th you have the floor! You can shine among your peers and make a bold statement about who you are without any ramifications whatsoever. You can exude confidence and this may have a lot to do with your choice of colours and jewellery.

Work and money

You may be performing your professional tasks excellently but could also doubt your role in the scheme of things. Between the 3rd and the 5th, you may need to re-examine your identity as a worker, as a contributor to the organisation you work for. This is all great stuff because it can help you reappraise your methods and adjust to bigger and better things.

You might be disappointed by the decision of a work colleague between the 6th and the 9th. This could be something associated with business or money and wasn't intended to hurt you in any way. You could be taking this matter far too personally. Let this slide so it doesn't interfere with what is otherwise a fairly good working relationship.

The fortunate planets, Jupiter and Venus, both go direct in their motion on the 19th, indicating a turning around for you in many areas of your life, particularly in your career and financial matters. Don't let overconfidence get the better of you.

Cut back waste on the 30th, otherwise you could get a rap on the knuckles for not being more attentive to the environmental issues at hand.

Destiny dates

Positive: 11, 12, 13, 14, 15, 16, 17, 18, 19, 25, 26

Negative: 1, 2, 21

Mixed: 3, 4, 5, 6, 7, 8, 9, 10, 22, 23, 24, 27, 28, 29, 30

Highlights of the month

The final month of the year promises to be both challenging and also somewhat frustrating. You may have plans and desires for your partner and yourself only to find that any suggestions you make are met with resistance, especially between the 1st and the 3rd. It's not a bad idea to communicate your intention before surprising someone. You might feel jaded buying a gift or organising an outing only to find that the response is less than lukewarm. Put the feelers out before investing emotional or financial resources so that you're not disappointed.

Your sexual energies are strong in the last month of 2010 as both Mercury and Mars trigger your carnal and lustful instincts to the max. Between the 6th and the 13th, you may find it hard reconciling these primal urges with what's been expected of you and how you've presented yourself in the past. You mustn't take yourself too seriously and try to incorporate a little bit of fun in this dramatic play of energies.

Between the 14th and the 18th, you might find the temptation to do something you wouldn't ordinarily do too hard to resist. Perhaps you'll find yourself in the company of a new group of people who are less inhibited and more prone to experimentation with new kinds of activities. It's very likely you'll want to indulge your fantasies and do something that would have shocked you years ago. But this too will be part of your learning curve and, as long as you don't let guilt get the better of you, it may be something you might be able to control.

From the 19th till the 25th, you must slow your pace because the complex aspect between Mars and the Sun makes you rash and accident-prone. There's a certain level of aggravation that may be hard for you to contain or to pinpoint. Direct action will be your favoured choice but may not yield the positive results you would hope for.

On the home front, this period requires you to be less demanding, particularly with youngsters. If you've let bad feelings build up over a period of time, this could be an explosive few days and it's not really the best time to vent your spleen with Christmas around the corner.

Making adjustments and finetuning your schedule for others for the sake of keeping the peace will be necessary between the 26th and the 31st. Eating a little humble pie will make sense to you, particularly as you'll be involved with a multitude of characters, all of whom may be too complex to balance under the circumstances.

By biting your tongue, you'll find that this will go a long way towards providing you with a peaceful conclusion to 2010.

Romance and friendship

Boring relationship? The Sun and Mars will see to it that your love life is anything *but* between the 1st and the 4th. These planets activate your level of discussion and interaction but may also rile you up. You and your partner could be at loggerheads over trifling matters on the home front. Control and moderation will be the key words.

You will require a balance between sensitivity, sentimentality and straight-up-and-down facts when you're dealing with friends on the 14th. You mustn't let your emotions get in the way of your negotiations because others will then see you as a pushover. You can continue to be direct but at the same time quietly assertive in the way you manage your friendships.

Your friends and family members want to dictate the course of events between the 18th and the 21st, but you mustn't let them do that. They could be confused and erratic in their own lives and, if you let them, this same pattern could wash over into your life. It's you who needs to run your show, on your terms, not theirs. Be strong and demand respect from everyone in the last month of the year.

With the Sun entering your zone of joint resources on the 22nd, it's quite likely that some serious discussions will take place surrounding how you are dealing with your finances. Try not to let these financial matters muddy the season's festivities. Postpone any talk of money and material differences until the new year.

Christmas will be a productive period, with Mars creating great aspects to your planets. This indicates a vibrant, up-beat and festive period for you. Take some care around the 30th when Mars and Saturn enter into a conflicting aspect, which may cause you some additional frustration, especially with youngsters.

Work and money

You'll be making an extra effort between the 1st and the 4th, given that it's the last month of the year. You could be following too many lines of thought at once for your own good, so stick to one path of action, even if others would have you believe that an alternative is better.

Have you got the right credentials to do what it is you want to do in life? You'll be thinking carefully along these lines so that you can improve your income and make the coming years more financially viable for yourself. You'll contemplate some new study course or perhaps even enrol in an educational institution between the 5th and the 8th.

Competitive energies heat up between the 16th and the 20th and you'll need to protect your turf to prove your worth. You need to channel your impulsiveness, and be patient and dedicated to the task at hand. Yet again, you'll be called upon to explain what your purpose or function in life is and, if you haven't thought about this, this last month of 2010 will bring these matters to the fore.

Pull all your financial resources together around the 22nd. Open a new bank account or transfer your savings to a higher-yielding investment.

The year 2010 finishes on a very financial note, but this should make you feel good as Jupiter continues to give you benefits on the work front for several more weeks.

Destiny dates

Positive: 1, 2, 3, 4, 5

Negative: 15, 16, 17, 18, 19, 20, 21, 23, 24, 25

Mixed: 6, 7, 8, 9, 10, 11, 12, 13, 14, 22, 26, 27, 28, 29, 30, 31

2010:
Astronumerology

*The more business a man has to do, the more he is able
to accomplish, for he learns to economize his time.*

—Sir Matthew Hale

The power behind your name

By adding the numbers of your name you can see
which planet is ruling you. Each of the letters of
the alphabet is assigned a number, which is listed
below. These numbers are ruled by the planets.
This is according to the ancient Chaldean system of
numerology and is very different to the Pythagorean
system to which many refer.

Each number is assigned a planet:

AIQJY	=	1	Sun
BKR	=	2	Moon
CGLS	=	3	Jupiter
DMT	=	4	Uranus
EHNX	=	5	Mercury
UVW	=	6	Venus
OZ	=	7	Neptune
FP	=	8	Saturn
—	=	9	Mars

Notice that the number 9 is not aligned with a letter
because it is considered special. Once the numbers
have been added you will see that a single planet

rules your name and personal affairs. Many famous actors, writers and musicians change their names to attract the energy of a luckier planet. You can experiment with the list and try new names or add the letters of your second name to see how that vibration suits you. It's a lot of fun!

Here is an example of how to find out the power of your name. If your name is John Smith, calculate the ruling planet by assigning each letter to a number in the table like this:

J O H N S M I T H
1 7 5 5 3 4 1 4 5

Now add the numbers like this:
$1 + 7 + 5 + 5 + 3 + 4 + 1 + 4 + 5 = 35$
Then add $3 + 5 = 8$

The ruling number of John Smith's name is 8, which is ruled by Saturn. Now study the name-number table to reveal the power of your name. The numbers 3 and 5 will also play a secondary role in John's character and destiny, so in this case you would also study the effects of Jupiter and Mercury.

Name-number table

Your name number	Ruling planet	Your name characteristics
1	**Sun**	Magnetic individual. Great energy and life force. Physically dynamic and sociable. Attracts good friends and individuals in powerful positions. Good government connections. Intelligent, impressive, flashy and victorious. A loyal number for relationships.
2	**Moon**	Soft, emotional nature. Changeable moods but psychic, intuitive senses. Imaginative nature and empathetic expression of feelings. Loves family, mother and home life. Night owl who probably needs more sleep. Success with the public and/or women.
3	**Jupiter**	Outgoing, optimistic number with lucky overtones. Attracts opportunities without trying. Good sense of timing. Religious or spiritual aspirations.

Your name number	Ruling planet	Your name characteristics
		Can investigate the meaning of life. Loves to travel and explore the world and people.
4	**Uranus**	Explosive character with many unusual aspects. Likes the untried and novel. Forward thinking, with many extraordinary friends. Gets fed up easily so needs plenty of invigorating experiences. Pioneering, technological and imaginative. Wilful and stubborn when wants to be. Unexpected events in life may be positive or negative.
5	**Mercury**	Quick-thinking mind with great powers of speech. Extremely vigorous life; always on the go and lives on nervous energy. Youthful attitude and never grows old. Looks younger than actual age. Young friends and humorous disposition. Loves reading and writing.
6	**Venus**	Delightful personality. Graceful and attractive character who cherishes friends

Your name number	Ruling planet	Your name characteristics
		and social life. Musical or artistic interests. Good for money making as well as abundant love affairs. Career in the public eye is possible. Loves family but is often overly concerned by friends.
7	Neptune	Intuitive, spiritual and self-sacrificing nature. Easily misled by those who need help. Loves to dream of life's possibilities. Has curative powers. Dreams are revealing and prophetic. Loves the water and will have many journeys in life. Spiritual aspirations dominate worldly desires.
8	Saturn	Hard-working, focused individual with slow but certain success. Incredible concentration and self-sacrifice for a goal.

Money orientated but generous when trust is gained. Professional but may be a hard taskmaster. Demands |

highest standards and needs to learn to enjoy life a little more.

| 9 | Mars | Fantastic physical drive and ambition. Sports and outdoor activities are keys to wellbeing. Confrontational. Likes to work and play just as hard. Caring and protective of family, friends and territory. Individual tastes in life but is also self-absorbed. Needs to listen to others' advice to gain greater success. |

Your 2010 planetary ruler

Astrology and numerology are very intimately connected. As already shown, each planet rules over a number between 1 and 9. Both your name *and* your birth date are ruled by planetary energies.

Add the numbers of your birth date and the year in question to find out which planet will control the coming year for you.

For example, if you were born on the 12th of November, add the numerals 1 and 2 (12, your day of birth) and 1 and 1 (11, your month of birth) to the year in question, in this case 2010 (the current year), like this:

$1 + 2 + 1 + 1 + 2 + 0 + 1 + 0 = 8$

The planet ruling your individual karma for 2010 will be Saturn because this planet rules the number 8.

You can even take your ruling name-number as shown earlier and add it to the year in question to throw more light on your coming personal affairs, like this:

John Smith = 8

Year coming = 2010

8 + 2 + 0 + 1 + 0 = 11

1 + 1 = 2

Therefore, 2 is the ruling number of the combined name and date vibrations. Study the Moon's number 2 influence for 2010.

Outlines of the year number ruled by each planet are given below. Enjoy!

1 is the year of the Sun

Overview

The Sun is the brightest object in the heavens and rules number 1 and the sign of Leo. Because of this the coming year will bring you great success and popularity.

You'll be full of life and radiant vibrations and are more than ready to tackle your new nine-year cycle, which begins now. Any new projects you commence are likely to be successful.

Your health and vitality will be very strong and your stamina at its peak. Even if you happen to have the odd problem with your health, your recuperative power will be strong.

You have tremendous magnetism this year so social popularity won't be a problem for you. I see many new friends and lovers coming into your life. Expect loads of invitations to parties and fun-filled outings. Just don't take your health for granted as you're likely to burn the candle at both ends.

With success coming your way, don't let it go to your head. You must maintain humility, which will make you even more popular in the coming year.

Love and pleasure

This is an important cycle for renewing your love and connections with your family, particularly if you have children. The Sun is connected with the sign of Leo and therefore brings an increase in musical and theatrical activities. Entertainment and other creative hobbies will be high on your agenda and bring you a great sense of satisfaction.

Work

You won't have to make too much of an effort to be successful this year because the brightness of the Sun will draw opportunities to you. Changes in work are likely and, if you have been concerned that opportunities are few and far between, 2010 will be different. You can expect some sort of promotion or an increase in income because your employers will take special note of your skills and service orientation.

Improving your luck

Leo is the ruler of number 1 and, therefore, if you're born under this star sign, 2010 will be particularly lucky. For others, July and August, the months of Leo, will bring good fortune. The 1st, 8th, 15th and 22nd hours of Sundays especially will give you a unique sort of luck in any sort of competition or activities generally. Keep your eye out for those born under Leo as they may be able to contribute something to your life and may even have a karmic connection to you. This is a particularly important year for your destiny.

Your lucky numbers in this coming cycle are 1, 10, 19 and 28.

2 is the year of the Moon
Overview

There's nothing more soothing than the cool light of the full Moon on a clear night. The Moon is emotional and receptive and controls your destiny in 2010. If you're able to use the positive energies of the Moon, it will be a great year in which you can realign and improve your relationships, particularly with family members.

Making a commitment to becoming a better person and bringing your emotions under control will also dominate your thinking. Try not to let your emotions get the better of you throughout the coming year because you may be drawn into the changeable nature of these lunar vibrations as well. If you fail to keep control of your emotional life you'll later regret some of your actions. You must blend careful thinking with feeling to arrive at the best results. Your luck throughout 2010 will certainly be determined by the state of your mind.

Because the Moon and the sign of Cancer rule the number 2 there is a certain amount of change to be expected this year. Keep your feelings steady and don't let your heart rule your head.

Love and pleasure

Your primary concern in 2010 will be your home and family life. You'll be finally keen to take on those renovations, or work on your garden. You may even think of buying a new home. You can at last carry out some of those plans and make your dreams come true. If you find yourself a little more temperamental than usual, do some extra meditation and spend time alone until you sort this out. You mustn't withhold your feelings from your partner as this will only create frustration.

Work

During 2010 your focus will be primarily on feelings and family; however, this doesn't mean you can't make great strides in your work as well. The Moon rules the general public and what you might find is that special opportunities and connections with the world at large present themselves to you. You could be working with large numbers of people.

If you're looking for a better work opportunity, try to focus your attention on women who can give you a hand. Use your intuition as it will be finely tuned this year. Work and career success depends upon your instincts.

Improving your luck

The sign of Cancer is your ruler this year and because the Moon rules Mondays, both this day of the week and the month of July are extremely lucky for you. The 1st, 8th, 15th and 22nd hours on Mondays will be very powerful. Pay special attention to the new and full Moon days throughout 2010.

The numbers 2, 11 and 29 are lucky for you.

3 is the year of Jupiter

Overview

The year 2010 will be a number 3 year for you and, because of this, Jupiter and Sagittarius will dominate your affairs. This is extremely lucky and shows you'll be motivated to broaden your horizons, gain more money and become extremely popular in your social circles. It looks like 2010 will be a fun-filled year with much excitement.

Jupiter and Sagittarius are generous to a fault and so, likewise, your open-handedness will mark the year. You'll be friendly and helpful to all of those around you.

Pisces is also under the rulership of the number 3 and this brings out your spiritual and compassionate nature. You'll become a much better person, reducing your negative karma by increasing your self-awareness and spiritual feelings. You will want to share your luck with those you love.

Love and pleasure

Travel and seeking new adventures will be part and parcel of your romantic life this year. Travelling to distant lands and meeting unusual people will open your heart to fresh possibilities of romance.

You'll try novel and audacious things and will find yourself in a different circle of friends. Compromise will be important in making your existing relationships work. Talk about your feelings. If you are currently in a relationship you'll feel an upswing in your affection for your partner. This is a perfect opportunity to deepen your love for each other and take your relationship to a new level.

If you're not yet attached to someone, there's good news for you. Great opportunities lie in store and a spiritual or karmic connection may be experienced in 2010.

Work

Great fortune can be expected through your working life in the next twelve months. Your friends and work colleagues will want to help you achieve your goals. Even your employers will be amenable to your requests for extra money or a better position within the organisation.

If you want to start a new job or possibly begin an independent line of business, this is a great year to do it. Jupiter looks set to give you plenty of opportunities, success and a superior reputation.

Improving your luck

As long as you can keep a balanced view of things and not overdo anything, your luck will increase dramatically throughout 2010. The important thing is to remain grounded and not be too airy-fairy about your objectives. Be realistic about your talents and capabilities and don't brag about your skills or achievements. This will only invite envy from others.

Moderate your social life as well and don't drink or eat too much as this will slow your reflexes and weaken your chances for success.

You have plenty of spiritual insights this year so you should use them to their maximum. In the 1st, 8th, 15th and 24th hours of Thursdays you should use your intuition to enhance your luck, and the numbers 3, 12, 21 and 30 are also lucky for you. March and December are your lucky months but generally the whole year should go pretty smoothly for you.

4 is the year of Uranus

Overview

The electric and exciting planet of the zodiac, Uranus, and its sign of Aquarius, rule your affairs throughout 2010. Dramatic events will surprise and at the same time unnerve you in your professional and personal life. So be prepared!

You'll be able to achieve many things this year and your dreams are likely to come true, but you mustn't be distracted or scattered with your energies. You'll be breaking through your own self-limitations and this will present challenges from your family and friends. You'll want to be independent and develop your spiritual powers and nothing will stop you.

Try to maintain discipline and an orderly lifestyle so you can make the most of these special energies this year. If unexpected things do happen, it's not a bad idea to have an alternative plan so you don't lose momentum.

Love and pleasure

You want something radical, something different in your relationships this year. It's quite likely that your love life will be feeling a little less than exciting so you'll take some important steps to change that. If your partner is as progressive as you'll be this year, then your relationship is likely to improve and fulfil both of you.

In your social life you will meet some very unusual people, whom you'll feel are especially connected to you spiritually. You may want to ditch everything for the excitement and passion of a completely new relationship, but tread carefully as this may not work out exactly as you expect it to.

Work

Technology, computing and the Internet will play a larger role in your professional life this coming year.

You'll have to move ahead with the times and learn new skills if you want to achieve success.

A hectic schedule is likely, so make sure your diary is with you at all times. Try to be more efficient and don't waste time.

New friends and alliances at work will help you achieve even greater success in the coming period. Becoming a team player will be even more important in gaining satisfaction from your professional endeavours.

Improving your luck

Moving too quickly and impulsively will cause you problems on all fronts, so be a little more patient and think your decisions through more carefully. Social, romantic and professional opportunities will come to you but take a little time to investigate the ramifications of your actions.

The 1st, 8th, 15th and 20th hours of any Saturday are lucky, but love and luck are likely to cross your path when you least expect it. The numbers 4, 13, 22 and 31 are also lucky for you this year.

5 is the year of Mercury

Overview

The supreme planet of communication, Mercury, is your ruling planet throughout 2010. The number 5, which is connected to Mercury, will confer upon you success through your intellectual abilities.

Any form of writing or speaking will be improved and this will be, to a large extent, underpinning your success. Your imagination will be stimulated by this planet, with many incredible new and exciting ideas coming to mind.

Mercury and the number 5 are considered somewhat indecisive. Be firm in your attitude and don't let too many ideas or opportunities distract and confuse you. By all means get as much information as you can to help you make the right decisions.

I see you involved with money proposals, job applications, even contracts that need to be signed, so remain as clear-headed as possible.

Your business skills and clear and concise communication will be at the heart of your life in 2010.

Love and pleasure

Mercury, which rules the signs of Gemini and Virgo, will make your love life a little difficult due to its changeable nature. On the one hand you'll feel passionate and loving to your partner, yet on the other you will feel like giving it all up for the excitement of a new affair. Maintain the middle ground.

Also, try not to be too critical with your friends and family members. The influence of Virgo makes you prone to expecting much more from others than they're capable of giving. Control your sharp tongue and don't hurt people's feelings. Encouraging others is the better path, leading to greater emotional satisfaction.

Work

Speed will dominate your professional life in 2010. You'll be flitting from one subject to another and taking on far more than you can handle. You'll need to make some serious changes in your routine to handle the avalanche of work that will come your way. You'll also be travelling with your work, but not necessarily overseas.

If you're in a job you enjoy then this year will give you additional successes. If not, it may be time to move on.

Improving your luck

Communication is the key to attaining your desires in the coming twelve months. Keep focused on one idea rather than scattering your energies in all directions and your success will be speedier.

By looking after your health, sleeping well and exercising regularly, you'll build up your resilience and mental strength.

The 1st, 8th, 15th and 20th hours of Wednesday are lucky so it's best to schedule your meetings and other important social engagements during these times. The lucky numbers for Mercury are 5, 14, 23 and 32.

6 is the year of Venus

Overview

Because you're ruled by 6 this year, love is in the air! Venus, Taurus and Libra are well known for their affinity with romance, love, and even marriage. If ever you were going to meet a soulmate and feel comfortable in love, 2010 must surely be your year.

Taurus has a strong connection to money and practical affairs as well, so finances will also improve if you are diligent about work and security issues.

The important thing to keep in mind this year is that sharing love and making that important soul connection should be kept high on your agenda. This will be an enjoyable period in your life.

Love and pleasure

Romance is the key thing for you this year and your current relationships will become more fulfilling if you happen to be attached. For singles, a 6 year heralds an important meeting that eventually leads to marriage.

You'll also be interested in fashion, gifts, jewellery and all sorts of socialising. It's at one of these social engagements that you could meet the love of your life. Remain available!

Venus is one of the planets that has a tendency to overdo things, so be moderate in your eating and drinking. Try generally to maintain a modest lifestyle.

Work

You'll have a clearer insight into finances and your future security during a number 6 year. Whereas previously you may have had additional expenses and extra distractions, your mind will now be more settled and capable of longer-term planning along these lines.

With the extra cash you might see this year, decorating your home or office will give you a special sort of satisfaction.

Social affairs and professional activities will be strongly linked. Any sort of work-related functions may offer you romantic opportunities as well. On the other hand, be careful not to mix up your work-place relationships with romantic ideals. This could complicate some of your professional activities.

Improving your luck

You'll want more money and a life of leisure and ease in 2010. Keep working on your strengths and eliminate your negative personality traits to create greater luck and harmony in your life.

Moderate all your actions and don't focus exclusively on money and material objects. Feed your spiritual needs as well. By balancing your inner and outer sides you'll see that your romantic and professional lives will be enhanced more easily.

The 1st, 8th, 15th and 20th hours on Fridays will be very lucky for you and new opportunities will arise for you at those times. You can use the numbers 6, 15, 24 and 33 to increase luck in your general affairs.

7 is the year of Neptune

Overview

The last and most evolved sign of the zodiac is

Pisces, which is ruled by Neptune. The number 7 is deeply connected with this zodiac sign and governs you in 2010. Your ideals seem to be clearer and more spiritually orientated than ever before. Your desire to evolve and understand your inner self will be a double-edged sword. It depends on how organised you are as to how well you can use these spiritual and abstract concepts in your practical life.

Your past hurts and deep emotional issues will be dealt with and removed for good, if you are serious about becoming a better human being.

Spend a little more time caring for yourself rather than others, as it's likely some of your friends will drain you of energy with their own personal problems. Of course, you mustn't turn a blind eye to the needs of others, but don't ignore your own personal requirements in the process.

Love and pleasure

Meeting people with similar life views and spiritual aspirations will rekindle your faith in relationships. If you do choose to develop a new romance, make sure there is a clear understanding of the responsibilities of one to the other. Don't get swept off your feet by people who have ulterior motives.

Keep your relationships realistic and see that the most idealistic partnerships must eventually come down to Earth. Deal with the practicalities of life.

Work

This is a year of hard work, but one in which you'll

come to understand the deeper significance of your professional ideals. You may discover a whole new aspect to your career, which involves a more compassionate and self-sacrificing side to your personality.

You'll also find that your way of working will change and you'll be more focused and able to get into the spirit of whatever you do. Finding meaningful work is very likely and therefore this could be a year when money, security, creativity and spirituality overlap to bring you a great sense of personal satisfaction.

Tapping into your greater self through meditation and self-study will bring you great benefits throughout 2010.

Improving your luck

Using self-sacrifice along with discrimination will be an unusual method of improving your luck. The laws of karma state that what you give, you receive in greater measure. This is one of the principal themes for you in 2010.

The 1st, 8th, 15th and 20th hours of Tuesdays are your lucky times. The numbers 7, 16, 25 and 34 should be used to increase your lucky energies.

8 is the year of Saturn

Overview

The earthy and practical sign of Capricorn and its ruler Saturn are intimately linked to the number

8, which rules you in 2010. Your discipline and far-sightedness will help you achieve great things in the coming year. With cautious discernment, slowly but surely you will reach your goals.

It may be that due to the influence of the solitary Saturn, your best work and achievement will be behind closed doors away from the limelight. You mustn't fear this as you'll discover many new things about yourself. You'll learn just how strong you really are.

Love and pleasure

Work will overshadow your personal affairs in 2010, but you mustn't let this erode the personal relationships you have. Becoming a workaholic brings great material successes but will also cause you to become too insular and aloof. Your family members won't take too kindly to you working 100-hour weeks.

Responsibility is one of the key words for this number and you will therefore find yourself in a position of authority that leaves very little time for fun. Try to make the time to enjoy the company of friends and family and by all means schedule time off on the weekends as it will give you the peace of mind you're looking for.

Because of your responsible attitude it will be very hard for you not to assume a greater role in your workplace and this indicates longer working hours with the likelihood of a promotion with equally good remuneration.

Work

Money is high on your agenda in 2010. Number 8 is a good money number according to the Chinese and this year is at last likely to bring you the fruits of your hard labour. You are cautious and resourceful in all your dealings and will not waste your hard-earned savings. You will also be very conscious of using your time wisely.

You will be given more responsibilities and you're likely to take them on, if only to prove to yourself that you can handle whatever life dishes up.

Expect a promotion in which you'll play a leading role in your work. Your diligence and hard work will pay off, literally, in a bigger salary and more respect from others.

Improving your luck

Caution is one of the key characteristics of the number 8 and is linked to Capricorn. But being overly cautious could cause you to miss valuable opportunities. If an offer is put to you, try to think outside the square and balance it with your naturally cautious nature.

Be gentle and kind to yourself. By loving yourself, others will naturally love you, too. The 1st, 8th, 15th and 20th hours of Saturdays are exceptionally lucky for you, as are the numbers 1, 8, 17, 26 and 35.

9 is the year of Mars

Overview

You are now entering the final year of a nine-year cycle dominated by the planet Mars and the sign of Aries. You'll be completing many things and are determined to be successful after several years of intense work.

Some of your relationships may now have reached their use-by date and even personal affairs may need to be released. Don't let arguments and disagreements get in the road of friendly resolution in these areas of your life.

Mars is a challenging planet, and this year, although you will be very active and productive, you may find others trying to obstruct the achievement of your goals. As a result you may react strongly to them, thereby creating disharmony in your workplace. Don't be so impulsive or reckless, and generally slow things down. The slower, steadier approach has greater merit this year.

Love and pleasure

If you become too bossy and pushy with friends this year you will just end up pushing them out of your life. It's a year to end certain friendships but by the same token it could be the perfect time to remove conflicts and thereby bolster your love affairs in 2010.

If you're feeling a little irritable and angry with those you love, try getting rid of these negative feelings through some intense, rigorous sports and physical activity. This will definitely relieve tension and improve your personal life.

Work

Because you're healthy and able to work at a more intense pace you'll achieve an incredible amount in the coming year. Overwork could become a problem if you're not careful.

Because the number 9 and Mars are infused with leadership energy, you'll be asked to take the reins of the job and steer your company or group in a certain direction. This will bring with it added responsibility but also a greater sense of purpose for you.

Improving your luck

Because of the hot and restless energy of the number 9, it is important to create more mental peace in your life this year. Lower the temperature, so to speak, and decompress your relationships rather than becoming aggravated. Try to talk with your work partners and loved ones rather than telling them what to do. This will generally pick up your health and your relationships.

The 1st, 8th, 15th and 20th hours of Tuesdays are the luckiest for you this year and, if you're involved in any disputes or need to attend to health issues, these times are also very good to get the best results. Your lucky numbers are 9, 18, 27 and 36.

GEMINI

2010:
Your Daily Planner

He who knows most grieves most for wasted time.

———Dante

According to astrology, the success of any venture or activity is dependent upon the planetary positions at the time you commence that activity. Electional astrology helps you select the most appropriate times for many of your day-to-day endeavours. These dates are applicable to each and every zodiac sign and can be used freely by one and all, even if your star sign doesn't fall under the one mentioned in this book. Please note that the daily planner is a universal system applicable equally to all *twelve* star signs. Anyone and everyone can use this planner irrespective of their birth sign.

Ancient astrologers understood the planetary patterns and how they impacted on each of us. This allowed them to suggest the best possible times to start various important activities. For example, many farmers still use this approach today: they understand the phases of the Moon, and attest to the fact that planting seeds on certain lunar days produces a far better crop than does planting on other days.

In the following section, many facets of daily life are considered. Using the lunar cycle and the combined strength of other planets allows us to work out the best times to do them. This is your personal almanac, which can be used in conjunction with any star sign to help optimise the results.

First, select the activity you are interested in, and then quickly scan the year for the best months to start it. When you have selected the month, you can finetune your timing by finding the best specific dates. You can then be sure that the planetary energies will be in sync with you, offering you the best possible outcome.

Coupled with what you know about your monthly and weekly trends, the daily planner is an effective tool to help you capitalise on opportunities that come your way this year.

Good luck, and may the planets bless you with great success, fortune and happiness in 2010!

Getting started in 2010

How many times have you made a new year's resolution to begin a diet or be a better person in your relationships? And, how many times has it not worked out? Well, part of the reason may be that you started out at the wrong time, because how successful you are is strongly influenced by the position of the Moon and the planets when you begin a particular activity. You will be more successful with the following endeavours if you start them on the days indicated.

Relationships

We all feel more empowered on some days than on others. This is because the planets have some power over us—their movement and their relationships to each other determine the ebb and flow of our energies. And, our levels of self-confidence and sense of romantic magnetism play an important part in the way we behave in relationships.

Your daily planner tells you the ideal dates for meeting new friends, initiating a love affair, spending time with family and loved ones—it even tells you the most appropriate times for sexual encounters.

You'll be surprised at how much more impact you will make in your relationships when you tune yourself in to the planetary energies on these special dates.

Falling in love/restoring love

During these times you could expect favourable energies to meet your soulmate or, if you've had difficulty in a relationship, to approach the one you love to rekindle both your and their emotional responses:

January	18, 20, 23, 24
February	15, 16, 20, 24
March	29
April	16
May	14, 17, 18, 19, 20, 23
June	14, 15, 16, 20, 21
July	12
August	10, 13, 14
September	9, 21, 22
October	8, 18, 19, 20
November	14, 15, 16, 19, 20, 21
December	13, 17, 18

Special times with friends and family

Socialising, partying and having a good time with those whose company you enjoy is highly favourable under the following dates. They are excellent to spend time with family and loved ones in a domestic environment:

January	6, 26, 27
February	12, 13, 14, 15, 16, 20, 24
March	11, 21, 22, 29, 30, 31
April	8
May	15, 16, 17, 18, 19, 20, 23, 24
June	1, 2, 3, 11, 12, 14, 15, 16, 20, 21, 29, 30
July	8, 9, 12, 17, 18, 26, 27
August	5, 6, 9, 10, 13, 14, 22, 23, 24
September	1, 2, 5, 9, 10, 18, 19, 20, 30
October	3, 19, 20, 25, 26, 30, 31
November	3, 4, 14, 15, 16, 22, 26, 27
December	2, 9, 10, 11, 19, 20, 24, 25

Healing or resuming relationships

If you're trying to get back together with the one you love or need a heart-to-heart or deep-and-meaningful discussion with someone, you can try the following dates to do so:

January	12, 13, 14, 15, 21, 22, 23, 24, 25
February	6
March	6, 31
April	2, 7, 8, 12, 16, 19, 23, 24, 25, 26

May	10, 11, 12, 13, 14, 15, 16, 17, 18, 19, 20, 21,22, 23, 24, 25, 26, 27, 28, 30
June	3, 8, 9, 10, 11, 12, 13, 14, 15, 16, 17, 21, 22, 23, 25, 26, 27, 28, 29, 30
July	1, 2, 3, 4, 5, 10, 11, 12, 13, 15, 16, 17, 18, 19, 20, 21, 22, 23, 28, 29, 30
August	1, 2, 3, 4, 5, 6, 9, 10, 13, 14, 15, 16, 20, 23, 25, 26, 27
September	2, 5, 9, 10, 13, 17, 18, 19, 20
October	1, 2, 3, 6, 12, 13, 14, 15, 20, 22, 23, 24, 25, 26, 27, 28, 29, 30, 31
November	3, 4, 5, 6, 7, 8, 9, 21, 27, 28, 29, 30
December	2, 3, 4, 6, 12, 13, 14, 17, 18, 19, 20, 21, 23, 24, 25

Sexual encounters

Physical and sexual energies are well favoured on the following dates. The energies of the planets enhance your moments of intimacy during these times:

January	1, 6, 7, 21, 22
February	6, 12, 13, 14, 20, 24
March	14, 15, 17, 18, 19, 30, 31
April	23, 24, 25, 26
May	9, 12, 14, 17, 18, 19, 20
June	3, 8, 9, 10, 11, 14, 15, 16, 20, 21, 29, 30
July	8, 9, 10, 11, 12
August	6, 10, 13, 14, 22, 23, 24

September   3, 4, 5, 6, 9, 10, 18, 19, 20, 21, 22, 30
October   1, 2, 3, 7, 8, 18, 19, 20, 23, 24, 28, 29, 30, 31
November   3, 4, 14, 15, 16, 19, 24, 25, 26, 27
December   2, 10, 11, 12, 13, 15, 16, 17, 19, 20, 22, 23,
             24, 25

Health and wellbeing

Your aura and life force are susceptible to the movements of the planets—in particular, they respond to the phases of the Moon.

The following dates are the most appropriate times to begin a diet, have cosmetic surgery, or seek medical advice. They also indicate the best times to help others.

Feeling of wellbeing

Your physical as well as your mental alertness should be strong on these following dates. You can plan your activities and expect a good response from others:

January   2, 3, 4, 5, 6, 7, 11, 12, 13, 14, 16, 17, 18,
             21, 22, 23, 24, 30, 31
February   1, 2, 7, 8, 15, 16, 17, 18, 19, 20, 21, 22, 23,
             24, 25, 26, 27, 28
March   16, 17, 18, 19, 20, 22, 23, 24, 25, 26, 27,
             28, 29
April   7, 13, 14, 16, 28
May   2, 11, 14, 25, 26
June   8, 22, 23, 26, 27, 28, 29, 30

July	4, 5, 8, 9, 12, 13, 14, 15, 16, 19, 20, 23, 24, 25
August	5, 6, 9, 10, 11, 12, 13, 15, 16, 20, 21
September	9, 10, 11, 12, 13, 16, 17, 21, 22, 24, 25, 28, 29, 30
October	3, 4, 5, 6, 7, 8, 9, 10, 13, 14, 15, 22
November	4, 5, 6, 10, 11, 19, 20, 21
December	7, 8, 17, 18, 28, 29

Healing and medicine

These times are good for approaching others who have expertise when you need some deeper understanding. They are also favourable for any sort of healing or medication and making appointments with doctors or psychologists. Planning surgery around these dates should bring good results.

Often giving up our time and energy to assist others doesn't necessarily result in the expected outcome. However, by lending a helping hand to a friend on the following dates, the results should be favourable:

January	1, 2, 3, 4, 6, 7, 8, 9, 11, 12, 13, 14, 15, 16, 17, 18, 19, 20, 21, 22, 23, 24, 26, 27, 28, 29, 30, 31
February	1, 5, 6, 9, 11, 12, 13, 14, 15, 16, 19
March	1, 2, 3, 4, 5, 8, 9, 10, 11, 12, 18, 19, 24, 25, 29
April	1, 3, 4, 5, 22, 26
May	4, 5

June	1, 2, 3, 9, 10, 17, 18, 22, 23, 24, 25, 29, 30
July	6, 7, 15, 16, 17, 18, 19, 21, 22, 23, 24, 25, 26
August	2, 3, 4, 11, 12, 17, 18, 19, 20, 21, 30, 31
September	6, 7, 8, 10, 11, 12, 13, 14, 15, 16, 17, 18, 26, 27, 28, 29
October	5, 7, 8, 9, 10, 11, 12, 13, 14, 15, 16, 17, 18, 19, 20, 21, 22, 23, 24, 25, 26, 28, 29, 30, 31
November	1, 2, 3, 5, 7, 8, 10, 11, 14, 15, 17, 18, 19, 22, 23
December	4, 5, 7, 8, 9, 10, 12, 13, 14, 16, 23, 24, 25, 26, 28, 29, 30, 31

Money

Money is an important part of life, and involves many decisions—decisions about borrowing, investing, spending. The ideal times for transactions are very much influenced by the planets, and whether your investment or nest egg grows or doesn't grow can often be linked to timing. Making your decisions on the following dates could give you a whole new perspective on your financial future.

Managing wealth and money

To build your nest egg it's a good time to open your bank account or invest money on the following dates:

January	1, 6, 7, 13, 14, 15, 18, 21, 22, 28, 29
February	3, 4, 9, 10, 11, 12, 13, 14, 15, 17, 18, 24, 25

March	2, 3, 9, 10, 16, 17, 18, 23, 24, 29, 30, 31
April	5, 6, 7, 13, 14, 19, 20, 21, 26, 27,
May	2, 3, 4, 10, 11, 17, 18, 23, 24, 30, 31
June	6, 7, 8, 13, 14, 19, 20, 21, 26, 27, 28
July	4, 5, 10, 11, 12, 17, 18, 23, 24, 25, 31
August	1, 7, 8, 13, 14, 20, 21, 27, 28, 29
September	3, 4, 9, 10, 16, 17, 23, 24, 25
October	1, 2, 7, 8, 13, 14, 15, 21, 22, 28, 29
November	3, 4, 10, 11, 17, 18, 24, 25
December	1, 2, 7, 8, 14, 15, 16, 21, 22, 23, 24, 29

Spending

It's always fun to spend but the following dates are more in tune with this activity and are likely to give you better results:

January	3, 4, 5, 6, 7, 8, 9, 10, 11, 12, 13, 14
February	3, 4, 5, 10, 19
March	8, 10, 11, 13, 14, 19
April	7, 8, 11, 12, 22
May	6, 7, 8, 9, 10, 11, 12, 13, 17, 18, 19, 20, 21, 22, 23, 24, 25, 26, 27, 28
June	1, 11, 12, 14, 16, 17, 19, 23, 25, 26, 27, 28, 29, 30
July	6, 7, 8, 23, 24, 25, 26, 27, 28, 29, 31
August	1, 2, 3, 4, 5, 15, 16, 17, 18, 19, 30, 31
September	1, 2, 3, 4, 17, 18, 19, 20, 21, 22, 23, 27, 28, 29, 30

October	4, 7, 12, 13, 14, 15, 16, 17, 18, 19, 27, 28
November	2, 3, 4, 25, 26, 27, 28
December	11, 22, 23

Selling

If you're thinking of selling something, whether it is small or large, consider the following dates as ideal times to do so:

January	18
February	12, 13, 14, 15
March	5, 6, 9, 14, 15, 16, 17, 18, 19, 21
April	1, 3, 4, 5, 22, 26
May	7, 12, 21, 29
June	3, 8, 9, 10, 11, 12, 13, 17, 24, 25, 26, 27, 28, 30
July	1, 2, 7, 9, 10, 11, 25, 27, 28, 29, 30, 31
August	1, 2, 3, 4, 5, 6, 7, 8, 9, 10, 13, 20, 23, 28
September	2, 9, 10, 11, 12, 13, 14, 15, 16, 17, 18, 19, 20, 21, 22, 23, 24, 26, 30
October	1, 2, 3, 4, 6, 7, 10, 11, 17, 18, 19, 20, 21, 22, 23, 24, 25, 27, 29
November	3, 4, 5, 6, 7, 11, 14, 15, 16, 17, 18, 19, 21, 23, 24, 25, 26, 27, 28, 29, 30
December	1, 2, 3, 4, 5, 6, 7, 8, 9, 10, 11, 12, 13, 14, 15, 16, 17, 18, 19, 20, 21, 22

Borrowing

Few of us like to borrow money, but if you must, taking out a loan on the following dates will be positive:

January	12, 30
February	7, 12, 13
March	6, 7, 8, 11
April	3, 4, 8
May	9, 28, 29
June	1, 2, 3, 4, 5, 29, 30
July	1, 2, 3, 26, 27, 28, 29, 30
August	9, 25, 26
September	5, 6
October	3, 30
November	26, 27
December	3, 4, 21, 22, 23, 30, 31

Work and education

Your career is important, and continual improvement of your skills is therefore also crucial professionally, mentally and socially. The dates below will help you find out the most appropriate times to improve your professional talents and commence new work or education associated with your work.

You may need to decide when to start learning a new skill, when to ask for a promotion, and even when to make an important career change. Here are the days when your mental and educational power is strong.

Learning new skills

Educational pursuits are lucky and bring good results on the following dates:

January	15, 16, 17, 18, 19, 20, 21, 22, 25, 26, 27
February	14, 15, 16, 17, 18, 19, 22, 23, 28
March	16, 17, 18, 21, 22, 27, 28
April	17, 18, 24, 25
May	15, 16, 21, 22
June	12, 17, 18, 24, 25
July	15, 16, 21, 22, 23, 24, 25
August	11, 12, 17, 18, 19
September	8, 13, 15, 20, 21, 22
October	11, 12
November	7, 8, 9
December	6, 19, 20

Changing career path or profession

If you're feeling stuck and need to move into a new professional activity, changing jobs could be done at these times:

January	6, 7, 15, 16, 17, 23, 24
February	12, 13, 14, 19, 20, 21
March	19, 20, 27, 28
April	15, 16, 24, 25
May	14, 21, 22
June	17, 18, 19, 20, 21
July	8, 9, 15, 16, 23, 24, 25

August	5, 6, 11, 12, 20, 21, 22, 23
September	1, 2, 8, 13, 14, 15, 17
October	8, 13, 14, 15, 16, 17
November	3, 4, 10, 11, 19, 20, 21
December	1, 2, 3, 7, 8, 17, 18, 28, 29

Promotion, professional focus and hard work

To increase your mental focus and achieve good results from the work you do; promotions are also likely on these dates:

January	4, 5, 6, 11, 12, 13, 14, 15, 16, 17, 18, 19, 21
February	6
March	16, 17, 18, 19, 20, 21, 23, 24, 25, 26, 27, 28, 29
April	8, 28, 29
May	12, 21
June	25, 26, 27, 28
July	4, 5, 8, 9, 12, 13, 14, 15, 16, 17, 18, 19, 20, 21, 22, 23, 24, 25, 26, 27
August	5, 6, 10, 11, 12, 13, 14, 15, 16, 17, 18, 19, 20, 21, 22, 23, 24
September	13, 14, 15
October	10, 11, 12, 13, 14, 15, 17, 18, 19, 20, 22, 23, 24, 30, 31
November	2, 4, 5, 6, 7, 8, 9, 23, 24, 25, 26, 27, 28, 29, 30
December	2, 3, 4, 11, 12, 13, 14, 15, 16, 18, 19, 20, 21, 23, 24, 25

Travel

Setting out on a holiday or adventurous journey is exciting. Here are the most favourable times for doing this. Travel on the following dates is likely to give you a sense of fulfilment:

January	15
February	15, 16, 18, 19, 20, 21
March	16, 17, 18, 21, 22, 23
April	19, 24, 25, 26, 27
May	16, 17, 18, 21, 22
June	17, 18, 19, 20, 21, 24, 25
July	21, 22, 23, 24, 25
August	19
September	9, 21, 22
October	18, 19, 20, 21, 22
November	7, 16, 17, 18
December	6, 14, 16, 19, 20

Beauty and grooming

Believe it or not, cutting your hair or nails has a powerful effect on your body's electromagnetic energy. If you cut your hair or nails at the wrong time of the month, you can reduce your level of vitality significantly. Use these dates to ensure you optimise your energy levels by staying in tune with the stars.

Hair and nails

January	1, 2, 3, 4, 5, 6, 7, 8, 11, 12, 13, 14, 15, 18, 19, 20, 21, 22, 25, 26, 27
February	3, 4, 5, 7, 8, 15, 16, 17, 18, 19, 22, 23, 24, 25
March	2, 3, 4, 6, 7, 8, 14, 15, 21, 22
April	1, 2, 3, 4, 5, 10, 11, 12, 17, 18, 19, 20, 21, 22, 23, 28, 29, 30
May	1, 2, 3, 4, 5, 7, 8, 9, 10, 11, 12, 13, 15, 16, 17, 18, 25, 26 27, 28, 29, 30
June	4, 5, 11, 12, 14, 15, 16, 24, 25
July	1, 2, 3, 8, 9, 12, 13, 14, 21, 22, 28, 29, 30
August	1, 2, 5, 6, 17, 18, 19, 25, 26
September	1, 2, 6, 7, 14, 15, 21, 22, 23, 24, 28, 29, 30
October	3, 4, 11, 12, 18, 19, 20, 25, 26, 27, 28, 29, 30
November	7, 8, 9, 14, 15, 16, 22, 23, 24, 25, 26, 27
December	5, 6, 12, 13, 19, 20, 21, 22, 23, 24, 25

Therapies, massage and self-pampering

January	6, 7, 13, 14, 15, 18, 19, 20, 21
February	2, 3, 9, 11, 14
March	1, 9, 14, 16, 17, 20, 23, 29
April	4, 5, 6, 10, 11, 12, 13, 17, 25, 26
May	2, 3, 7, 8, 9, 10, 11, 14, 15, 16, 17, 22, 23, 24, 31
June	3, 5, 12, 18, 19, 26, 27
July	4, 7, 8, 9, 10, 16, 23, 28, 29, 30, 31
August	3, 4, 5, 6, 7, 13, 20, 21, 24, 25, 26, 27, 28, 31
September	2, 17, 21, 28, 29

October	13, 14, 15, 18, 19, 21, 25, 26, 27, 28
November	2, 3, 9, 11, 14, 15, 16, 17, 21, 24, 29
December	7, 12, 13, 14, 15, 18, 19, 20, 22, 26, 27, 28, 29

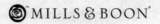

millsandboon.co.uk Community

Join Us!

The Community is the perfect place to meet and chat to kindred spirits who love books and reading as much as you do, but it's also the place to:

- Get the inside scoop from authors about their latest books
- Learn how to write a romance book with advice from our editors
- Help us to continue publishing the best in women's fiction
- Share your thoughts on the books we publish
- Befriend other users

Forums: Interact with each other as well as authors, editors and a whole host of other users worldwide.

Blogs: Every registered community member has their own blog to tell the world what they're up to and what's on their mind.

Book Challenge: We're aiming to read 5,000 books and have joined forces with The Reading Agency in our inaugural Book Challenge.

Profile Page: Showcase yourself and keep a record of your recent community activity.

Social Networking: We've added buttons at the end of every post to share via digg, Facebook, Google, Yahoo, technorati and de.licio.us.

www.millsandboon.co.uk

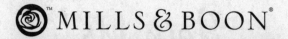